Study Guide

GCSE
Success

AQA
Maths

AQA Maths

GCSE
Success

Gillian Rich

Contents

4 Geometry and measures

Your GCSE course

AQA offers two GCSE Mathematics specifications. Each has two entry tiers, Foundation and Higher. There are a range of grades available:

Tier	Grade
Foundation	C–G
Higher	A*–D (E allowed)

From June 2014, 100% of the assessment is terminal (i.e. it will take place at the end of the course).

GCSE Mathematics A (3 units)(4360): Foundation and Higher

This is available for assessment in November and June and consists of three unit papers.

Statistics and Number (calculator):	Unit 1F: 1hr, 54 marks, 26.7%
	Unit 1H: 1hr, 54 marks, 26.7%
Number and Algebra (non-calculator):	Unit 2F: 1hr 15mins, 66 marks, 33.3%
	Unit 2H: 1hr 15mins, 66 marks, 33.3%
Geometry and Algebra (calculator):	Unit 3F: 1hr 30mins, 80 marks, 40%
	Unit 3H: 1hr 30mins, 80 marks, 40%

Unit 1 papers assess all the statistics and probability content of the specification. Some appropriate aspects of number are also tested.

Unit 2 papers assess the number and algebra topics which do not need a calculator.

Unit 3 papers assess all the geometry and measures content of the specification. Algebra topics requiring a calculator and graphical methods of algebra are also tested.

In this book, the specification labels at the start of each section show you which units the information is relevant to.

GCSE Mathematics B (Linear)(4365): Foundation and Higher

This is available for assessment in November and June and consists of two papers.

Foundation:
Paper 1F (non-calculator):	1hr 15mins, 70 marks, 40%
Paper 2F (calculator):	1hr 45mins, 105 marks, 60%

Higher:
Paper 1H (non-calculator):	1hr 30mins, 70 marks, 40%
Paper 2H (calculator):	2hrs, 105 marks, 60%

All content can be assessed on either paper so you should revise all topics in this book before your exams.

For full details of the specifications go to www.aqa.org.uk

Five ways to improve your grade

1. Preparation

- Make a list of **revision topics** and leave plenty of time to revise.
- Check that all your **maths equipment** is ready for the exam. You need a pen, pencil, ruler, rubber, pencil sharpener, protractor, pair of compasses and calculator.
- Make sure you know how to use your **calculator** efficiently – read the instruction book!
- Learn the different methods of working through a question.
- **Practise** answering questions under timed conditions.

2. Instructions

- Make sure you know how long the exam lasts and the end time. You should then be able to **pace yourself** through the paper.
- **Read carefully** the instructions on the front of the exam paper.
- Some **formulae** are printed inside the cover of the exam paper. Remember that they are there – you may need to use them.
- You must use a pen to write on the exam paper, but make sure you use a pencil for graphs and diagrams; if you make a mistake it is easier to correct.
- Write all working and answers in the spaces provided.
- You must answer all questions to obtain full marks. At least make an attempt at all questions because it is better than leaving a question out completely.

3. Questions

- **Read every question carefully**, so you know what is required.
- Do not spend too much time on a question. You can come back to it later.
- Marks allocated and space given are an indication of the length of answer required.
- Questions with more marks are usually divided into smaller steps. Work through the question from the first step.
- **Method marks** are given for each step even if the final answer is incorrect.
- Even **rough working** must be written on your exam paper – it is the only paper you will have.
- Do not do your rough working on your hand, pencil case or any other surface. You cannot give it in, so the examiner will not see it and you may lose marks.

4. Working

- **Graphs** must be drawn with a sharp pencil, never pen. Remember to label axes.
- Always give **units** in the answers if they are not provided.
- Answers must be given to an **appropriate degree of accuracy**.
- Write down the **calculator display** in full. Leave **rounding and correction** until the final answer, unless directed otherwise.
- Marks are given for **method, facts and answers**.
- If an incorrect answer is given without working, the mark will be zero.
- All your **written work must be clear**. The examiner is not used to your handwriting. Untidy, confused and messy answers can be misread and lose marks.

5. Checking

- Check that all answers are sensible in the context of the question.
- Check that you have answered or attempted every question. Have you missed anything? It would be a shame to lose marks because you have turned over two pages at once!
- Check through your paper for at least 10 minutes before the examination ends.

If you have prepared and revised well, you can approach the examination calmly and with confidence. Good luck!

How to use this book

What this book covers

- *GCSE Success AQA Maths* provides full coverage of all the content and skills on the AQA examination board specifications. It is divided into four chapters:

  Chapter 1: Statistics and probability

  Chapter 2: Number

  Chapter 3: Algebra

  Chapter 4: Geometry and measures
- The content is accessible to students working at both Foundation and Higher Tier levels.
- The practice questions reflect the level of questions on the Higher Tier exam papers. They are intended to be challenging to help you push yourself to achieve the best possible grade.

Functional skills

Functional skills are skills that help you in everyday and real life situations. They are an important part of the new GCSE Mathematics courses. This book includes questions that require you to apply your knowledge of maths to solve problems relevant to real life.

How this book will help you

- The specification labels show you which units the information is relevant to.

- If you are taking the linear course all the content can be assessed on either paper.

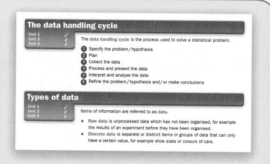

- Key points highlight important revision facts and methods.

- Important mathematical terms are highlighted in bold. Make sure you understand what these terms mean.

- Useful hints in the margin give guidance and focus your attention on important revision tips.

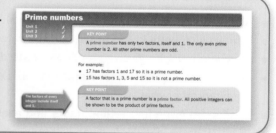

- Worked examples take you through calculations and problem solving one step at a time.

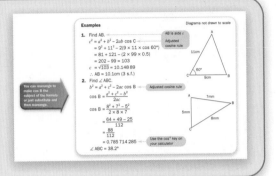

- Progress checks and exam practice questions help you to confirm your understanding of the topic.

- You will need to do your working and write your answers on a separate piece of paper. Check your answers against those in the book. If some are incorrect, then go back over the topic to see where you went wrong.

- 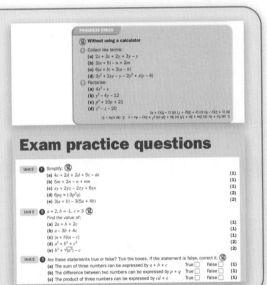 This icon indicates that the question should be attempted without a calculator.

- Sample GCSE questions are given with model answers and advice on how to gain the most marks.

- The unit numbers alongside the questions refer to the three-unit specification. Remember that Unit 2 is a non-calculator paper.

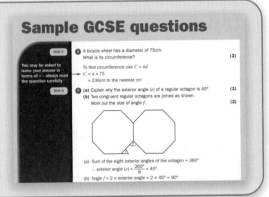

Notes

1 Statistics and probability

The following topics are covered in this chapter:

- **Collecting and organising data**
- **Presenting and interpreting data**
- **Averages**
- **Probability**
- **Theoretical probability and relative frequency**
- **Probability rules**
- **Tree diagrams**

1.1 Collecting and organising data

LEARNING SUMMARY

After studying this section, you should be able to understand:

- the data handling cycle
- types of data
- sampling
- collection and organisation of data

The data handling cycle

Unit 1	✓
Unit 2	✗
Unit 3	✗

The **data handling cycle** is the process used to solve a statistical problem.

1. Specify the problem / hypothesis
2. Plan
3. Collect the data
4. Process and present the data
5. Interpret and analyse the data
6. Refine the problem / hypothesis and / or make conclusions

Types of data

Unit 1	✓
Unit 2	✗
Unit 3	✗

Items of information are referred to as **data**.

- **Raw data** is unprocessed data which has not been organised, for example the results of an experiment before they have been organised.
- **Discrete data** is separate or distinct items or groups of data that can only have a certain value, for example shoe sizes or colours of cars.

- **Continuous data** is data that has been arranged into groups with no gaps that can have any value, for example measurements of heights of plants.
- **Grouped data** is information that has been organised into groups, for example age groups of a population.
- **Primary data** is original information that is collected from questionnaires, surveys or experiments, for example results obtained by tossing a coin.
- **Secondary data** is information that has been taken from printed books and tables or the Internet, for example league tables of schools.
- **Qualitative data** is descriptive data, for example types of vehicles in a car park.
- **Quantitative data** is data that gives measurement. This can be either in discrete or continuous form, for example the number of pupils in a class is discrete quantitative data and the height of pupils in a class is continuous quantitative data.

Sampling

Unit 1	✓
Unit 2	✗
Unit 3	✗

Although population usually refers to the number of people living in a place, it is also used for a large group of items under investigation.

When conducting a survey, it is impossible to deal with large numbers. It is more appropriate to use a **sample** instead. The sample must be large enough to significantly represent the whole group or population.

A sample should be **unbiased**, so must not tend towards particular results. For example, asking opinion about a new product after free samples are given would bias the results.

Sampling can be done in different ways.

Random sampling

Random sampling means having an equal chance of being selected. It is very difficult to get a perfectly random sample, although a computer can generate random numbers.

Systematic sampling

Systematic sampling uses a rule to pick a sample, for example choosing to question every 10th person walking down a street. This may be biased by choosing a particular street or standing in a particular place. The weather or time of day can also change a sample.

Stratified sampling can be found on higher level papers.

Stratified sampling

Stratified sampling takes into account the differences in the composition of a population. This is used to eliminate bias. Samples are taken from each part of the population. They are proportional to the size of the group.

KEY POINT

Stratified sample of a group = $\dfrac{\text{size of group}}{\text{size of population}} \times \text{size of sample}$

For example:

Different travel arrangements of pupils in a school are to be surveyed.

Total number in school = 1100. It is decided to use a sample of 100.

Year	Number in year	Stratified sample
7	190	$\frac{190}{1100} \times 100 = 17$
8	220	$\frac{220}{1100} \times 100 = 20$
9	250	$\frac{250}{1100} \times 100 = 23$
10	240	$\frac{240}{1100} \times 100 = 22$
11	200	$\frac{200}{1100} \times 100 = 18$

> Remember to calculate the stratified sample to the nearest whole number. You cannot have part of a person!

Quota sampling

Market researchers tend to use **quota sampling**. They may choose to question a given number of men in a certain age group or a group of people in a particular occupation. Bias can be introduced by the choice of interviewees.

Collection and organisation of data

Unit 1   ✓
Unit 2   ✗
Unit 3   ✗

KEY POINT

Data collection can be done by designing a questionnaire for a survey, observation or experiment. Responses can also be recorded in a data collection sheet or table. The information collected produces a database.

Questionnaire

A questionnaire is a set of questions designed to find data about a particular topic. The questions must be easy to understand, unbiased and asked in a logical order.

They should produce answers that are easy to analyse.
- Use **closed questions** as they can be answered by a single word or phrase, for example 'How many CDs do you have?'
- Try not to use **open questions** as they allow for many answers, for example, 'What do you think of this CD?'
- Do not use **leading questions** as they put the questioner's opinion into the mind of the interviewee, for example 'Don't you think ten CDs is too many to have of one band?'
- **Response boxes** should be provided for answers where possible, for example yes ☐ no ☐ ; 1 ☐ 2 ☐ 3 ☐

Observation

If collecting data by observation, write a list of what data you need in order to answer the given question. For example, to answer the question 'How many vehicles pass a certain point during a certain time?' you would need to...
- make a list of all possible vehicles
- divide the total time into smaller slots
- collect data from both sides of the road
- record the vehicles on a data collection sheet.

Organising data

- A **frequency table** is any table displaying primary or secondary observation data, which is arranged in columns to show the frequency of events.

  For example:

Vehicles (10–11am)	Frequency	Vehicles (10–11am)	Frequency
Bike	3	Taxi	2
Motorbike	2	Van	4
Car	13	Truck	3
Bus	5	Other	1
		Total	**33**

Use 'other' in the table for any vehicle not included, such as a caravan.

- A **tally chart** has a mark for each observation. This is useful when conducting an experiment. When filling in tally charts, mark I for each vehicle. The 5th mark goes across the previous four marks to make JHT. It is easier to count in 5s, so mistakes are avoided.

Vehicle	Tally	Frequency
Bike	III	3
Motorbike	II	2
Car	JHT JHT III	13
Bus	JHT	5
Taxi	II	2
Van	IIII	4
Truck	III	3
Other	I	1
Total	**10–11am**	**33**

- A **two-way table** illustrates two different variables. This two-way table records whether the vehicles, in the above survey, were used privately or commercially.

Vehicle	Bike	Motorbike	Car	Bus	Taxi	Van	Truck	Other
Private	3	1	11	0	0	1	0	1
Commercial	0	1	2	5	2	3	3	0

Class intervals

When collecting continuous data, such as heights or weights, it is convenient to divide it into groups or **class intervals**. For example, this table shows the percentage of women of each age group in part-time work:

Make sure that the upper class limit is not used as the lower class limit in the next interval. You cannot have 21–25 and 25–30 and so on in this table.

Age	21–24	25–29	30–34	35–39	40–44	45–49	50–54	55–59
%	20	32	50	52	48	47	52	58

The class intervals are usually even, but not always.

Experiment

A **hypothesis** is a theory that is tested to see if it is true.

To test a hypothesis, you need to set up an experiment. Make sure the experiment produces enough results to produce a significant conclusion.

For example:

Hypothesis: 'Height affects shoe size.'

1. Measure height and shoe size using samples of different groups of people. Make sure the sample is of a sufficient size and reflects the total population being tested.
2. Record results on a data collection sheet.
3. Organise data into a table, such as a tally chart or two-way table.
4. Decide whether the hypothesis is true based on the results.

PROGRESS CHECK

1. What type of data are the following?
   (a) Javelin lengths recorded at the last Olympic Games.
   (b) Types of coffee sold at a café during one week.
   (c) Brands of cat food available at a local supermarket.
2. The following questions are taken from a survey on TV sport programmes. Suggest how they can be improved.
   (a) How old are you?
   (b) What type of sport do you prefer to watch on TV?
   Tennis ❑   Football ❑   Cricket ❑   Golf ❑
   (c) Do you agree that TV sport programmes are better than they used to be?
3. The secretary of a fan club collects data about its 1600 members.

Age	<20	20–30	31–40	>40
Male	205	310	152	53
Female	224	396	210	50

He would like to take a stratified sample of 80 people based on age and gender.
   (a) Calculate the number of people from each group that would be used in the sample.
   (b) What do you notice about your answers?

(b) Stratified sample adds up to 82 because of rounding up to whole numbers

Age	<20	20–30	31–40	>40
Male	$\frac{205}{1600} \times 80 = 10$	$\frac{310}{1600} \times 80 = 16$	$\frac{152}{1600} \times 80 = 8$	$\frac{53}{1600} \times 80 = 3$
Female	$\frac{224}{1600} \times 80 = 11$	$\frac{396}{1600} \times 80 = 20$	$\frac{210}{1600} \times 80 = 11$	$\frac{50}{1600} \times 80 = 3$

3. (a)

Worse ❑ Don't know ❑
you think that TV sports programmes are better or worse than they used to be?' Better ❑
included   (c) biased and leading question – change it to an unbiased closed question, e.g. 'Do
qualitative, discrete   2. (a) give groups of ages <10 ❑, 20–30 ❑, etc.   (b) 'other' should be
1. (a) secondary, quantitative, continuous   (b) primary, qualitative, discrete   (c) primary,

1.2 Presenting and interpreting data

LEARNING SUMMARY	**After studying this section, you should be able to understand:** • charts • diagrams • graphs

Charts

Unit 1	✓
Unit 2	✗
Unit 3	✗

Once data has been recorded and sorted in a table, it can be presented in the form of a chart.

Pictogram

A **pictogram** is a chart that uses pictures to represent the numbers of items.

> **Example**
>
> The following table gives the number of red, blue, silver and black cars passing a certain point. Present the information as a pictogram.
>
> | Colour of car | Red | Blue | Silver | Black |
> |---|---|---|---|---|
> | Frequency | 20 | 13 | 10 | 6 |
>
>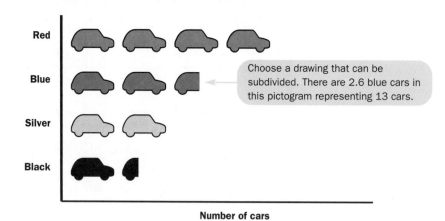
>
> Choose a drawing that can be subdivided. There are 2.6 blue cars in this pictogram representing 13 cars.
>
> **Number of cars**
>
> **Key:**
>
> = 5 cars

> You must include a key to your pictures.

Bar chart

> If bars are used horizontally, the axes are reversed.

A **bar chart** uses bars of equal width to represent frequency. The bars are usually vertical. Frequency is marked on the vertical axis. Items or groups of items are marked on the horizontal axis. Use a bar chart if the number of items is small.

For example, this bar chart shows the number of rainy days over four months.

Number of rainy days	Jul	Aug	Sept	Oct
Frequency	12.5	8	4	12

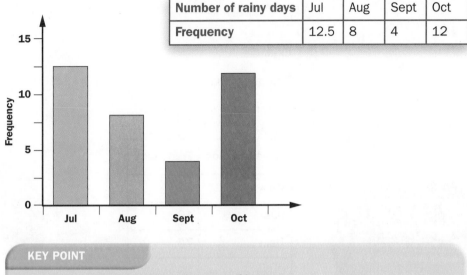

A bar–line graph uses lines instead of bars.

Two or more distributions can be compared by using a **dual bar chart** (also known as a comparative or multiple bar chart). For example, this dual bar chart compares across and down clues in a crossword. It shows that the down clues generally have fewer letters in their answer.

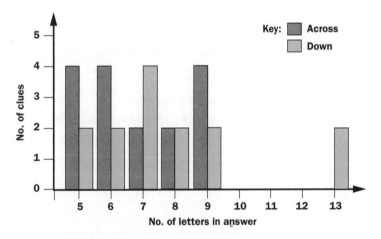

A composite bar chart compares two or more distributions on each bar. For example, this composite bar chart compares the activities chosen by students in each school year. The total number of students in each year can be read off the individual bars, e.g. there are 90 students in year 7.

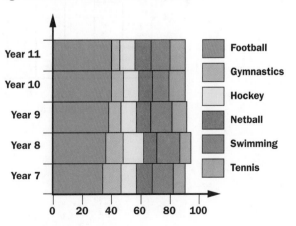

Pie chart

A **pie chart** is a circular chart that uses sectors in proportion to value.

Example

Draw a pie chart to show the way in which 360 pupils travel to the local school.

Sector angle = $\dfrac{\text{value}}{\text{total}} \times 360°$

Travel method	Frequency
Walk	135
Bus	120
Train	75
Cycle	30
Total	**360**

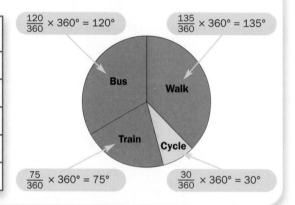

$\frac{120}{360} \times 360° = 120°$

$\frac{135}{360} \times 360° = 135°$

$\frac{75}{360} \times 360° = 75°$

$\frac{30}{360} \times 360° = 30°$

> Mark the centre and one radius. Measure the first angle from here.
>
> The sum of the sector angles should equal 360°.
>
> You must label your diagram.

Two or more distributions can be compared by comparing sectors of their pie charts. A pie chart only shows proportions so remember to take the individual populations into account.

Histogram

A **histogram** is a chart that uses bars to represent continuous grouped data. There are no gaps between the bars in a histogram.

● **Equal class intervals**

If the class intervals are equal, frequency is proportional to the heights of the bars. The vertical axis shows the frequency. The horizontal axis is divided into equal class intervals.

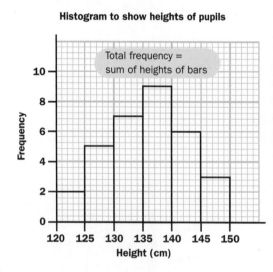

Histogram to show heights of pupils

Total frequency = sum of heights of bars

Height (cm)	Frequency
$120 \leqslant h < 125$	2
$125 \leqslant h < 130$	5
$130 \leqslant h < 135$	7
$135 \leqslant h < 140$	9
$140 \leqslant h < 145$	6
$145 \leqslant h < 150$	3
Total	**32**

Histograms with unequal class intervals can be found on higher level papers.

- **Unequal class intervals**

  If the class intervals are unequal, frequency is proportional to the areas of the bars. This is called frequency density. Work out frequency density using:

  $$\text{Frequency density} = \frac{\text{frequency}}{\text{class width interval}}$$

  Draw the histogram using frequency density on the vertical axis and class width on the horizontal axis.

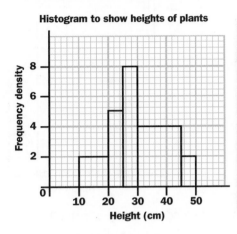

Histogram to show heights of plants

Height (cm)	Freq. (f)	Class width	Frequency density
$10 \leqslant h < 20$	20	10	$20 \div 10 = 2$
$20 \leqslant h < 25$	25	5	$25 \div 5 = 5$
$25 \leqslant h < 30$	40	5	$40 \div 5 = 8$
$30 \leqslant h < 45$	60	15	$60 \div 15 = 4$
$45 \leqslant h < 50$	10	5	$10 \div 5 = 2$
Total	**155**		

If you are provided with a histogram it is possible to find out the frequencies, the modal class and the median of the data.

For example, if you were given the histogram above:

- First draw up a table, filling in the heights, class widths and frequency densities from the histogram.
- Work out frequency (f) as shown below.

Height (cm) (class interval)	Class width	Frequency density	Frequency (f) (class width × frequency density)
$10 \leqslant h < 20$	10	2	$10 \times 2 = 20$
$20 \leqslant h < 25$	5	5	$5 \times 5 = 25$
$25 \leqslant h < 30$	5	8	$5 \times 8 = 40$
$30 \leqslant h < 45$	15	4	$15 \times 4 = 60$
$45 \leqslant h < 50$	5	2	$5 \times 2 = 10$
		Total	**155**

Modal class = $30 \leqslant h < 45$ ← This class has the highest frequency

See pages 24–25 for modal class and median.

The median is the middle value, when placed in ascending order. There are 155 plants, so the middle value is the 78th. This is in the $25 \leqslant h < 30$ class. ← This class goes from 46th value to the 85th value

Frequency polygon

To draw a **frequency polygon** you need to plot the frequency at the midpoint of each class interval.

> A frequency polygon can be drawn without the histogram.

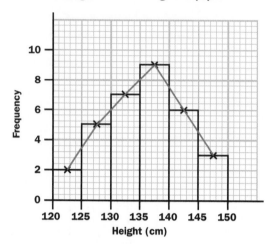

Histogram to show heights of pupils

Distributions can be compared by drawing their frequency polygons on the same axes.

Diagrams

Unit 1	✓
Unit 2	✗
Unit 3	✗

The distribution of data can be displayed in the form of a diagram.

Stem-and-leaf diagram

A stem-and-leaf diagram is used for displaying data. It is useful for showing the shape of a distribution.

For example:
Here are the marks gained by 12 pupils in a Maths test.

20	30	20	15	22	17	16	22	27	8	29	25

The marks can be illustrated on a stem-and-leaf diagram.
- The tens digit of each value forms the 'stem'.
- The units digit of each value forms the 'leaf'.

> Put the values in order, before writing them out.

```
0 | 8                          Mark is 8
1 | 5  6  7                    Marks are 15, 16, 17
2 | 0  0  2  2  5  7  9        Marks are 20, 20, 22, and so on
3 | 0                          Mark is 30
```

From the stem-and-leaf diagram above, you can identify certain information:
- The modal group, the one with the highest frequency, is the 20–29 group.
- There are 12 results so the median result is mid-way between the 6th and 7th result. The 6th result is 20 and the 7th result is 22 so the median is 21.

> See pages 24–25 for modal class and median.

Two distributions may be compared by using a common stem, with leaves that go back-to-back.

Box plot diagrams are sometimes called box and whisker diagrams.

See pages 24–26 for median and quartiles.

Box plot diagrams can be found on higher level papers.

Box plot diagram

Box plot diagrams display shape, range, median and quartiles.

For example:
A maths teacher recorded the times that a Year 7 class spent on their maths homework one night. The table shows the times, to the nearest minute, after they have been arranged in order, from smallest to largest:

12	16	16	18	18	18	18	19	19
19	20	20	21	21	21	21	21	21
25	26	27	29	29	30	30		

The smallest value = 12, the largest value = 30.
The median is the 13th value = 21.
The lower quartile is the median of the data to the left of the actual median:

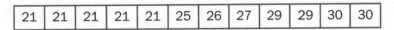

12	16	16	18	18	18	18	19	19	19	20	20

Lower quartile = 18

The upper quartile is the median of the data to the right of the actual median:

21	21	21	21	21	25	26	27	29	29	30	30

Upper quartile = 25.5

You can now draw a box plot for the data. The 'box' stretches from 18, (the lower quartile), to 25.5, (the upper quartile). The median is shown inside the box at 21, and the 'whiskers' stretch from the lower quartile to the smallest value, 12, and from the upper quartile to the highest value, 30.

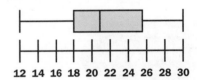

12 14 16 18 20 22 24 26 28 30

Box plots can be very useful in giving a quick 'picture' of a distribution and for comparing two distributions:

- If the median is in the middle of the box, the distribution of data is symmetrical.
- If the median is nearer the lower quartile, the distribution of data is positively skewed.
- If the median is nearer the upper quartile, the distribution of data is negatively skewed.

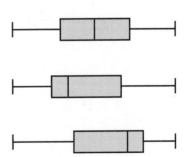

Graphs

Graphs are another way of presenting data.

Scatter graph

A **scatter graph** (or scatter diagram) is useful when comparing two sets of variables. The variables are plotted against each other. The relationship between them is called **correlation**.

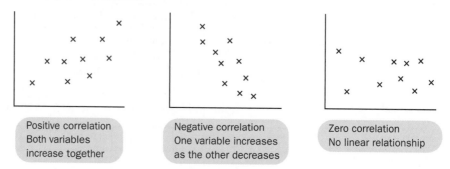

Positive correlation
Both variables increase together

Negative correlation
One variable increases as the other decreases

Zero correlation
No linear relationship

If the points are almost in a straight line, there is a strong correlation. Otherwise they may have a moderate or weak correlation.

If there is a strong correlation, a **line of best fit** can be drawn. This shows the trend. It should go through the middle of the set of points. It can be used to predict values beyond those plotted.

> If just one point is outside the general trend, this may be a 'rogue' point, so check it carefully.

Rogue value sits outside plotted range

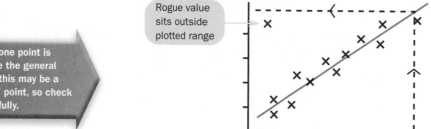

Time–series graph

Time–series graphs show trends over time or seasons. They have time on the horizontal axis.

For example, the changes in a patient's temperature can be shown on a time–series graph.

The data only uses 36–40°C, so use a zig-zag line at the lower end of the axis.

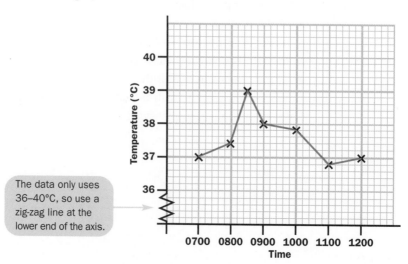

Cumulative frequency graph

Cumulative frequency graphs can be found on higher level papers.

The **cumulative frequency** tells you how often a result was obtained that was less than or equal to a given value in a collection of data. Cumulative frequency is found by adding together the frequencies to give a running total.

For example:
The marks gained in a Maths test were recorded in a cumulative frequency table. The cumulative frequency is found by adding each value to the sum of all the previous values.

You will usually be given all the values in the question and have to sort them into groups yourself.

Mark group	Frequency (f)	Upper limit of the group	Cumulative frequency
1–10	2	≤ 10	2
11–20	10	≤ 20	2 + 10 = 12
21–30	15	≤ 30	15 + 12 = 27
31–40	20	≤ 40	20 + 27 = 47
41–50	16	≤ 50	16 + 47 = 63
51–60	12	≤ 60	12 + 63 = 75

(Total frequency = 75)

A cumulative frequency graph may have points joined using a ruler.

A cumulative frequency graph is drawn using the cumulative frequency table. The points are plotted at the upper limit of each group and then connected with a smooth curve.

See page 26 for how to interpret cumulative frequency graphs.

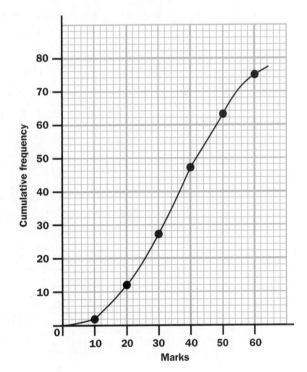

Misleading graphs

Graphs, charts and diagrams are used to illustrate data. Unfortunately they are sometimes used to distort statistics. Do not take these illustrations at face value.

Beware of **misleading graphs** that use...

- a frequency axis not starting at zero to distort shape
- unequal intervals on the frequency axis
- 3D to change perspective in bar charts, pie charts and pictograms
- unequal sized pictures in pictograms
- axes without labels and graphs without scales
- comparisons that do not start from the same level.

PROGRESS CHECK

1. Calculate the sector angles for a pie chart to represent the favourite ethnic foods of a group of friends.

Type of food	Italian	Chinese	Mexican	French	Middle Eastern	Indian
Frequency	10	16	6	8	4	16

2. Calculate frequency density for this data about heights of flowers in a garden.

Height of flower (h) in metres	< 2	$2 \leqslant h < 3$	$3 \leqslant h < 5$	$5 \leqslant h < 7$	$7 \leqslant h < 8$	$\geqslant 8$
Frequency	2	8	12	10	4	0

3. These scatter graphs illustrate data collected by a garage about the value of three different cars.

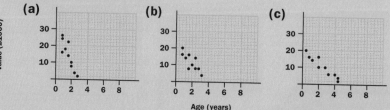

State the correlation for each. What can be said about the connection between age and value of the cars?

3. a) Negative b) Negative c) Negative; The older the car, the lower the value

Height of flower (h) in metres	< 2	$2 \leqslant h < 3$	$3 \leqslant h < 5$	$5 \leqslant h < 7$	$7 \leqslant h < 8$	$\geqslant 8$
Frequency density	1	8	6	5	4	0

2.

Type of food	Italian	Chinese	Mexican	French	Middle Eastern	Indian
Angle	60°	96°	36°	48°	24°	96°

1.

1.3 Averages

Mean, median, mode and range

Unit 1	✓
Unit 2	✗
Unit 3	✗

The **mean**, **median** and **mode** are all **averages**. Average is the term given to a representative value.

Mean

> **KEY POINT**
>
> Mean = $\dfrac{\text{total sum of values}}{\text{number of values}}$

Examples

1. Calculate the mean from the following list of values.

   12.3cm, 14cm, 10.5cm, 11.7cm, 9cm

   Mean = $\dfrac{(12.3 + 14 + 10.5 + 11.7 + 9)}{5}$ = 11.5cm ⟵ Number of values

   Check that the answer lies between the smallest and largest values.

2. Calculate the mean from the following frequency table.

Mins. taken to complete question (x)	Number of students (f)	$f \times x = fx$
7	2	14
9	5	45
11	4	44
12	2	24
Total	**13**	**127**

   Divide total of fx products by total frequency:

   Mean = $\dfrac{\Sigma fx}{\Sigma f} = \dfrac{127}{13}$ = 9.8mins (2 s.f.)

   Σ is a Greek letter standing for 'sum of'.

You cannot calculate the exact value of the mean when the data is grouped or continuous. You can only estimate it using the midpoint of each group.

> **KEY POINT**
>
> Estimated mean = $\dfrac{(\text{midpoint of each group} \times \text{frequency})}{\text{total frequency}}$

Example

A sample of apples is weighed when picked. Calculate an estimated mean from the data in the table below.

Weight (g)	Frequency (f)	Midpoint (m)	fm (f x m)
$100 \leqslant w < 110$	5	105	525
$110 \leqslant w < 120$	7	115	805
$120 \leqslant w < 130$	12	125	1500
$130 \leqslant w < 140$	8	135	1080
$140 \leqslant w < 150$	4	145	580
Total	**36**		**4490**

Estimated mean $= \dfrac{\Sigma fm}{\Sigma f} = \dfrac{4490}{36} = 124.7\text{g}$

Median

KEY POINT

The median is the middle value in an ascending sequence of values.

Examples

1. Find the median length of each set of discrete data.

(a) 3cm, 3cm, 1cm, 1.5cm, 2cm, 2cm, 2.5cm

First, rearrange in ascending order:
1cm, 1.5cm, 2cm, 2cm, 2.5cm, 3cm, 3cm
There are seven values so the median is the 4th value.
The median is 2cm.

Count to check all values are included.

(b) 5km, 8km, 4km, 4km, 6km, 6km

4km, 4km, 5km, 6km, 6km, 8km ← Rearrange
There are six values so the median is halfway between the 3rd and 4th values.
The median is 5.5km.

2. Find the median weight of apples from the data in the table below.

Weight (g)	Frequency (f)
$100 \leqslant w < 110$	5
$110 \leqslant w < 120$	7
$120 \leqslant w < 130$	12
$130 \leqslant w < 140$	8
$140 \leqslant w < 150$	4
Total	**36**

As this is continuous grouped data find the group, or class, that contains the middle value. The middle value is halfway between the 18th and 19th values. Starting with the lowest weight, you will find that the 18th and 19th values are in the $120 \leqslant w < 130$ group.

∴ median group is $120 \leqslant w < 130$

Mode

> **KEY POINT**
>
> The mode is the most frequent value.

Examples

1. Find the mode of the following discrete data.
   0, 3, 2, 5, 5, 2, 3, 1, 2, 0, 2

   The most frequent number is 2. This is the mode.

2. Find the mode of weights of apples from the data in the table below.

Weight (g)	Frequency (f)
$100 \leqslant w < 110$	5
$110 \leqslant w < 120$	7
$120 \leqslant w < 130$	12
$130 \leqslant w < 140$	8
$140 \leqslant w < 150$	4
Total	**36**

As this is continuous grouped data, find the group, or class, with the highest frequency.
This is $120 \leqslant w < 130$.
This is called the **modal class**.

Range

> **KEY POINT**
>
> The **range** is the spread of data.
> Range = greatest value − least value

Another word for spread is dispersion.

Examples

Find the range of each set of data.
(a) 0, 3, 2, 5, 5, 2, 3, 1, 2, 0, 2

Range = 5 − 0 = 5

(b) 12.3cm, 14cm, 10.5cm, 11.7cm, 9cm

Range = 14cm − 9cm = 5cm

Using appropriate averages

When choosing which average to use, think about the context of the question:
- The mean gives a typical value. It uses all the values including the extremes.
- The median is useful if there are extreme values.
- The mode gives the most common value.

Quartiles and inter-quartile range

Unit 1 ✓
Unit 2 ✗
Unit 3 ✗

Quartiles and inter-quartile range can be found on higher level papers.

KEY POINT

A **quartile** is one of three values, which divides a frequency distribution into four intervals.
- **Lower quartile** (LQ) is one-quarter of the way through the data.
- **Median** is halfway through the data.
- **Upper quartile** (UQ) is three-quarters of the way through the data.

The **inter-quartile range** (IQ) = upper quartile – lower quartile.

The inter-quartile range measures spread; it is the middle 50% of the distribution of the data.

Interpreting cumulative frequency graphs

See page 21 for cumulative frequency graphs.

Once you have drawn a cumulative frequency graph you can compare the distribution of the data.

Cumulative frequency graphs can be found on higher level papers.

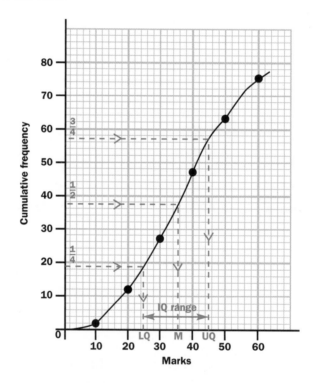

- Mark the median at halfway up the cumulative frequency axis, the upper quartile at three-quarters of the way up and the lower quartile at one-quarter of the way up.
- Draw horizontal dotted lines from these points to meet the curve.
- Draw vertical dotted lines from where they meet the curve to meet the horizontal axis.

Use the median and quartiles to compare distributions.

- These points give the median, upper quartile and lower quartile of the distribution.
- The inter-quartile range can now be calculated: IQ = UQ – LQ = 45 – 25 = 20

PROGRESS CHECK

1 Calculate the mean, mode and median of the following:
   (a) Heights: 135cm, 136cm, 136cm, 135cm, 136cm, 137cm, 140cm
   (b) Weights: 26kg, 27kg, 27kg, 28kg, 29kg, 29kg, 30kg
   (c) Times: 35s, 36s, 37s, 37s, 38s, 38s, 38s

2 Find the modal class and estimated mean of...
   (a) Heights of trees

Height (h) m	< 10	$10 \leqslant h < 20$	$20 \leqslant h < 30$	$30 \leqslant h < 40$
Frequency (f)	20	19	21	4

   (b) Test marks

Marks (m)	< 10	$10 \leqslant m < 15$	$15 \leqslant m < 20$	$20 \leqslant m < 25$	$25 \leqslant m < 30$
Freq. (f)	14	26	16	6	2

3 Work out the cumulative frequencies for this table showing ages of people living in a block of flats. Draw a cumulative frequency graph and find the median and inter-quartile range.

Age (a)	< 15	$15 \leqslant a < 30$	$30 \leqslant a < 45$	$45 \leqslant a < 60$	$60 \leqslant a < 80$
Frequency (f)	28	70	54	32	16

1. (a) Mean = 136.4cm, Mode = 136cm, Median = 136cm (b) Mean = 28kg, Mode = 27kg/29kg, Median = 28kg (c) Mean = 37s, Mode = 38s, Median = 37s 2. (a) Modal class = 20 < h > 30, Estimated mean = 16.4m (b) Modal class = 10 ≤ m < 15, Estimated mean = 13.5 3. Cumulative frequencies = 28, 98, 152, 184, 200; Median = 32, IQ range = 24

1.4 Probability

LEARNING SUMMARY

After studying this section, you should be able to understand:
● probability vocabulary
● probability scale

Probability vocabulary

Unit 1	✓
Unit 2	✗
Unit 3	✗

The **probability** of an event occurring is the chance that it may happen. This can be given as a fraction, decimal or percentage. The result of an event is an **outcome**.

KEY POINT

Probability (P) = $\dfrac{\text{number of times an event can happen}}{\text{total number of possible outcomes}}$

> **Example**
>
> A dice is thrown. There are six possible outcomes: 1, 2, 3, 4, 5 or 6.
>
> **(a)** What is the probability of throwing a 6?
>
> $$P(\text{throwing a 6}) = \frac{1}{6}$$
>
> **(b)** What is the probability of throwing an even number?
>
> $$P(\text{throwing an even number}) = \frac{3}{6} = \frac{1}{2}$$

> If you are giving an answer in fraction form, give it in its lowest terms.

> The phrase 'mutually exclusive' may not be used in the exam.

Mutually exclusive events are events that cannot happen at the same time. For example, if a dice is thrown, the events 'obtaining a 1' and 'obtaining an even number' are mutually exclusive as they cannot happen at the same time.

Here is some **vocabulary** that you are likely to come across in probability questions:
- **Certain**: P(certain event) = 1
  For example, P(Tuesday follows Monday) = 1
- **Likely**: P(likely event) is between 0.5 and 1
  For example, P(goal will be scored in Saturday's match) = 0.75
  (Very likely is used at the upper end)
- **Evens**: P(even chance event) = $\frac{1}{2}$ or 0.5 or 50%
  For example, P(getting heads when tossing a coin) = 0.5
- **Unlikely**: P(unlikely event) is between 0 and 0.5
  For example, P(snow will fall in November) = 0.2
  (Very unlikely is used at the lower end)
- **Impossible**: P(impossible event) = 0
  For example, P(scoring 15 when throwing two dice) = 0

It is also useful to learn the following facts:
- A pack of cards consists of 52 cards. There are two red suits (hearts and diamonds) and two black suits (spades and clubs). Each suit has 13 cards (numbers 2–10, Jack, Queen, King and Ace). There may be two Jokers in the pack, but these are rarely used in questions.
- A fair dice has a $\frac{1}{6}$ chance of showing numbers 1–6 when thrown. A fair coin has an even chance of showing heads or tails when tossed. Biased or weighted dice and coins will not produce these outcomes.

Probability scale

Unit 1	✓
Unit 2	✗
Unit 3	✗

A range of probabilities can be shown on a **probability scale**.

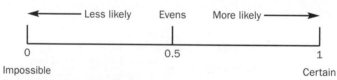

> **PROGRESS CHECK**
>
> 🖩 **Without using a calculator**
>
> 1. All the black cards are removed from a pack of cards. State whether it is likely, unlikely, evens, certain or impossible that a card picked from the remaining cards is...
>   **(a)** a diamond   **(b)** a black card   **(c)** a picture card.

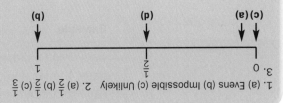
1.5 Theoretical probability and relative frequency

LEARNING SUMMARY

After studying this section, you should be able to understand:

- estimating probability
- relative frequency graphs
- outcomes of single events
- outcomes of two successive events
- sample space diagrams
- probability of an event not happening

Estimating probability

Unit 1   ✓
Unit 2   ✗
Unit 3   ✗

Probability can be predicted, or estimated, by using experimental data.

- **Theoretical probability** predicts the likelihood of an event occurring if all outcomes are equally likely, i.e. it is what we expect will happen.

> **KEY POINT**
>
> Theoretical probability = $\dfrac{\text{number of times an event can happen}}{\text{total number of possible outcomes}}$

For example, the probability of throwing a 6 with a fair dice is predicted to be $\frac{1}{6}$.

- **Relative frequency** allows you to estimate how many times an event may occur, during a number of trials. Experimental data can be used to find relative frequency.

> **KEY POINT**
>
> Relative frequency = $\dfrac{\text{number of successful trials}}{\text{total number of trials}}$

The more times an experiment is repeated, the closer the outcome will be to the theoretical probability. For example, if you throw a fair dice 12 times, you would expect each number to appear twice, because the theoretical probability equals $\frac{1}{6}$ each time. However, it is unlikely that this will happen with only 12 throws. If you were to continue the experiment for 1200 throws though, it should even out so that each number appears 200 times.

If a dice is thrown 600 times and the number 6 appears 200 times, you have to consider if the dice is fair. You would normally expect $\frac{1}{6} \times 600 = 100$ times.

Example

Sam drops a drawing pin on the floor 10 times. He notes that it falls on its base 4 times and on its side 6 times.

(a) Estimate the number of times the drawing pin will fall on its base and the number of times it will fall on its side if Sam drops the pin 100 times in total.

Number of times pin falls on base = 4 when dropped 10 times

$$\therefore \text{ relative frequency} = \frac{4}{10} = 0.4$$

$0.4 \times 100 = 40$ when dropped 100 times

Number of times pin falls on side = 6 when dropped 10 times

$$\therefore \text{ relative frequency} = \frac{6}{10} = 0.6$$

$0.6 \times 100 = 60$ when dropped 100 times

(b) Emma drops the same pin 300 times. She works out that the relative frequency of the pin falling on its side is 0.67
How many times did the pin fall on its side?

Use the formula for relative frequency:
Number of times pin falls on side = 0.67×300
= 201 times ← Relative frequency × total number of trials

Relative frequency graphs

Unit 1	✓
Unit 2	✗
Unit 3	✗

Relative frequency graphs can be found on higher level papers.

Relative frequency graphs are a useful way of comparing experimental and theoretical data.

For example:
A coin is tossed 150 times. The number of heads after each ten trials is recorded in a table and the relative frequency is plotted on a graph.

The relative frequency is $\frac{\text{Total number of heads}}{\text{Total number of trials}}$

Number of trials (n)	Number of heads (h)	Relative frequency ($h \div n$)
1–10	3	$\frac{3}{10} = 0.3$
11–20	6	$\frac{9}{20} = 0.45$
21–30	7	$\frac{16}{30} = 0.53$
↓	↓	↓
141–150	4	$\frac{74}{150} = 0.49$

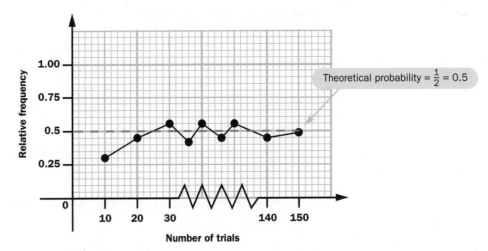

Theoretical probability = $\frac{1}{2}$ = 0.5

> If you do not believe this, try it for yourself!

You should find that, as the number of trials increases, the plotted line tends to get closer and closer to the theoretical line.

Outcomes of single events

Unit 1	✓
Unit 2	✗
Unit 3	✗

You may have to find the probability of single events.

Example

A bag contains 4 red balls, 5 blue balls, 3 green balls and 8 white balls. A ball is picked at random. Find the probability of picking...

(a) a green ball

$$P(\text{green}) = \frac{3}{20}$$

> $\dfrac{\text{Number of green balls}}{\text{Total number of balls}}$

(b) a red ball

$$P(\text{red}) = \frac{4}{20} = \frac{1}{5}$$

> Give in lowest terms. $\frac{1}{5}$ can also be given as 0.2 or 20%

(c) a black ball

$$P(\text{black}) = 0$$

> Impossible as there are no black balls

Outcomes of two successive events

Unit 1	✓
Unit 2	✗
Unit 3	✗

Dependent events

One event may be dependent on the outcome of a previous event. This is called **conditional probability**.

Example

A bag contains 2 red counters, 2 white counters and 2 blue counters. A counter is picked at random.

(a) What is the probability of picking a red counter?

$$P(\text{red}) = \frac{2}{6} = \frac{1}{3}$$

(b) What is the probability of picking a blue counter if the red counter is not replaced?

$$P(\text{blue}) = \frac{2}{5}$$

> There are now only 5 counters as one has been removed

Independent events

Two events are independent if the outcome of one event has no effect on the outcome of the other event.

> **Example**
>
> Minnie tosses two coins, one at a time.
> **(a)** What is the probability of Minnie tossing a head with the first coin?
> $$P(\text{head}) = \frac{1}{2}$$
> **(b)** What is the probability of Minnie tossing a head with the second coin?
> $$P(\text{head}) = \frac{1}{2}$$

Sample space diagrams

Unit 1	✓
Unit 2	✗
Unit 3	✗

It is often necessary to list all the possible outcomes of two events. This should be done logically otherwise some outcomes may be missed.

All outcomes can be displayed in a **sample space diagram**.

> **Example**
>
> **(a)** List all the outcomes of throwing two dice.
>
> | | | First dice | | | | | |
> |---|---|---|---|---|---|---|---|
> | | | **1** | **2** | **3** | **4** | **5** | **6** |
> | | **1** | 1/1 | 1/2 | 1/3 | 1/4 | 1/5 | 1/6 |
> | | **2** | 2/1 | 2/2 | 2/3 | 2/4 | 2/5 | 2/6 |
> | Second dice | **3** | 3/1 | 3/2 | 3/3 | 3/4 | 3/5 | 3/6 |
> | | **4** | 4/1 | 4/2 | 4/3 | 4/4 | 4/5 | 4/6 |
> | | **5** | 5/1 | 5/2 | 5/3 | 5/4 | 5/5 | 5/6 |
> | | **6** | 6/1 | 6/2 | 6/3 | 6/4 | 6/5 | 6/6 |
>
> The possible outcomes of each dice are listed in row 1 and column 1. Each cell gives the two numbers on the dice.
>
> **(b)** Find the probability of both dice showing the same number.
> Total number of outcomes = 6 × 6 = 36
> $$P(\text{same number}) = \frac{6}{36} = \frac{1}{6}$$ ← There are 6 cells with the same two numbers

Probability of an event not happening

Unit 1	✓
Unit 2	✗
Unit 3	✗

KEY POINT

The sum of probabilities equals 1 as the total probability is certain.
This means that:

P(event will happen) = 1 − P(event will not happen)

P(event will not happen) = 1 − P(event will happen)

Example

The probability that it will rain on Monday is $\frac{5}{20}$. What is the probability that it will not rain on Monday?

P(will not rain on Monday) = 1 − P(will rain on Monday)

$$= 1 - \frac{5}{20}$$
$$= 1 - \frac{1}{4}$$
$$= \frac{3}{4}$$

PROGRESS CHECK

1. A spinner is spun 40 times.
   The pointer lands 18 times on 1, 10 times on 2 and 12 times on 3.
   (a) Calculate the relative frequency of landing on each number.
   (b) Estimate the number of times the pointer would land on each number if the spinner is spun 480 times.

2. If each letter of the word MATHEMATICS is written on a separate card, what is the probability of picking the letter…
   (a) E **(b)** M **(c)** P?

3. Two coins are tossed. Draw a sample space diagram for all possible outcomes. What is the probability of getting a head and a tail?

4. Throw a dice 240 times. Record the number of sixes after each 10 trials in a table.
   Draw a relative frequency graph for your results.

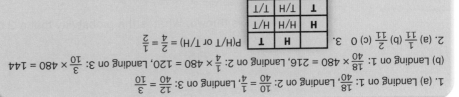

4. As the number of trials increases, the plotted line will get closer to $\frac{1}{6}$ (0.16 or approx. 0.2)

	H	T
H	H/H	H/T
T	T/H	T/T

P(H/T or T/H) = $\frac{2}{4} = \frac{1}{2}$

2. (a) $\frac{1}{11}$ (b) $\frac{2}{11}$ (c) 0   3.

(b) Landing on 1: $\frac{18}{40} \times 480 = 216$, Landing on 2: $\frac{1}{4} \times 480 = 120$, Landing on 3: $\frac{3}{10} \times 480 = 144$

1. (a) Landing on 1: $\frac{18}{40}$; Landing on 2: $\frac{10}{40} = \frac{1}{4}$; Landing on 3: $\frac{12}{40} = \frac{3}{10}$

1.6 Probability rules

Probability rules

Unit 1   ✓
Unit 2   ✗
Unit 3   ✗

Probability rules can be found on higher level papers.

Independent events

The outcome of independent events can be worked out using a probability rule.

> **KEY POINT**
>
> If A and B are two independent events, then the probability of A and B occurring can be calculated using:
>
> P(A and B) = P(A) × P(B)
>
> If there are more events, they can be included as in:
>
> P(A and B and C) = P(A) × P(B) × P(C)

Example

A dice is thrown and a card is picked from a pack.
What is the probability that a 6 is thrown and the Queen of Hearts is picked?

These events are independent of one another.

$P(6) = \dfrac{1}{6}$ $P(\text{Queen of Hearts}) = \dfrac{1}{52}$

$P(6 \text{ and Queen of Hearts}) = \dfrac{1}{6} \times \dfrac{1}{52} = \dfrac{1}{312}$

Mutually exclusive events

Mutually exclusive events can be worked out using a probability rule.

> **KEY POINT**
>
> If A and B are mutually exclusive events, then the probability of A or B occurring can be calculated using:
>
> P(A or B) = P(A) + P(B)

Example

A dice is thrown. What is the probability that a 3 or 5 is thrown?

$P(3) = \dfrac{1}{6}$ $P(5) = \dfrac{1}{6}$

$P(3 \text{ or } 5) = \dfrac{1}{6} + \dfrac{1}{6} = \dfrac{2}{6} = \dfrac{1}{3}$

This is the opposite of what you would expect. 'And' does not mean +.

The two probability rules on page 34 are also known as the **AND / OR rules**.
- If 'and' is used in the question P(A) *and* P(B), then multiply probabilities.
- If 'or' is used in the question P(A) *or* P(B), then add probabilities.

PROGRESS CHECK

 Without using a calculator

One pile of cards is marked with letters A–F and another pile of cards is marked G–L. A card is picked from each pile.
What is the probability of getting…
(a) two vowels
(b) two consonants
(c) an E or F together with a K or L?

(a) $\frac{2}{36} = \frac{1}{18}$ (b) $\frac{20}{36} = \frac{5}{9}$ (c) $\frac{4}{36} = \frac{1}{9}$

1.7 Tree diagrams

LEARNING SUMMARY	After studying this section, you should be able to understand:
	• drawing and using tree diagrams

Drawing and using tree diagrams

Unit 1	✓
Unit 2	✗
Unit 3	✗

A **tree diagram** can be used to show all the possible outcomes of an event. Tree diagrams can illustrate dependent, independent and mutually exclusive events.

Tree diagrams can be found on higher level papers.

Each branch on a tree diagram gives a possible outcome for an event. The probability is written on the branch.

Independent and mutually exclusive events

Example

A coin is tossed three times. A tree diagram represents these events.
(a) Find the probability of getting three tails
(b) Find the probability of getting at least one head and one tail.

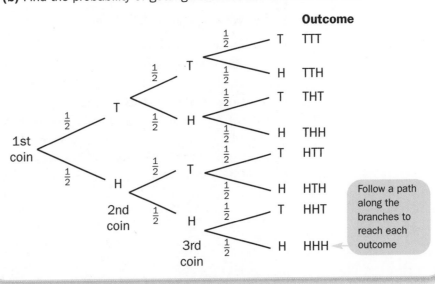

Follow a path along the branches to reach each outcome

(a) Multiply probabilities for outcome of three throws.

(tail *and* tail *and* tail → use AND rule)

$$P(\text{three tails}) = \frac{1}{2} \times \frac{1}{2} \times \frac{1}{2} = \frac{1}{8}$$

(b) There are six outcomes giving at least one head and one tail.

(TTH *or* THT *or* THH *or* HTT *or* HTH *or* HHT → use OR rule)

$$P(\text{at least one head and one tail}) = \frac{1}{8} + \frac{1}{8} + \frac{1}{8} + \frac{1}{8} + \frac{1}{8} + \frac{1}{8} = \frac{6}{8} = \frac{3}{4}$$

Dependent events (conditional probability)

Example

A bag contains 10 green marbles and 5 yellow marbles.

A marble is picked out of the bag and not replaced. This is repeated.

Find the probability of...

(a) picking one marble of each colour **(b)** not picking a yellow

(c) picking two marbles of the same colour.

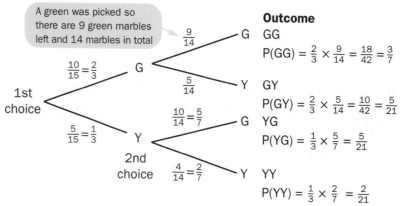

A green was picked so there are 9 green marbles left and 14 marbles in total

Outcome

GG $\quad P(GG) = \frac{2}{3} \times \frac{9}{14} = \frac{18}{42} = \frac{3}{7}$

GY $\quad P(GY) = \frac{2}{3} \times \frac{5}{14} = \frac{10}{42} = \frac{5}{21}$

YG $\quad P(YG) = \frac{1}{3} \times \frac{5}{7} = \frac{5}{21}$

YY $\quad P(YY) = \frac{1}{3} \times \frac{2}{7} = \frac{2}{21}$

(a) P(one of each colour) $= \frac{5}{21} + \frac{5}{21} = \frac{10}{21}$

(b) P(not yellow) $= \frac{3}{7}$

(c) P(both same colour) $= \frac{3}{7} + \frac{2}{21} = \frac{9}{21} + \frac{2}{21} = \frac{11}{21}$

PROGRESS CHECK

🖩 **Without using a calculator**

1 Use tree diagrams for these questions.

This spinner is used in a game. It is spun two times.

What is the probability of getting...

(a) an odd number both times?

(b) two numbers adding up to an even number?

2 The probability of Ayesha passing her Maths Paper A is 0.7 and Paper B is 0.6. What is the probability of Ayesha...

(a) passing both papers? **(b)** passing one paper? **(c)** failing both papers?

1. (Tree diagram has four arms, each with four further arms. There are 16 outcomes.

Probability of each outcome $= \frac{1}{4} \times \frac{1}{4} = \frac{1}{16}$)

(a) P(odd number both times) $= \frac{4}{16} = \frac{1}{4}$ (b) P(two numbers adding up to even number) $= 8 \times \frac{1}{16} = \frac{8}{16} = \frac{1}{2}$

2. (Tree diagram has two arms, each with two further arms. There are four outcomes)

(a) P(passing both) $= 0.7 \times 0.6 = 0.42$ (b) P(passing one) $= 0.28 + 0.18 = 0.46$

(c) P(fail both) $= 0.3 \times 0.4 = 0.12$

Sample GCSE questions

Unit 1

1 Esther has three striped scarves: brown and cream, brown and beige, brown and orange. She has two pairs of gloves: brown, beige.

(a) Complete the table to show all combinations of scarves and gloves that Esther could wear. **(2)**

Scarf	Gloves
Brown and cream	Brown
Brown and cream	Beige

(b) Esther was in a hurry this morning. She picked a scarf and a pair of gloves at random. What is the probability that the scarf and gloves she chose were not coloured orange? **(2)**

(a)

Scarf	Gloves
Brown and cream	Brown
Brown and cream	Beige
Brown and beige	Brown
Brown and beige	Beige
Brown and orange	Brown
Brown and orange	Beige

Remember to include all combinations of the colours

(b) P(no orange colour) = $\frac{4}{6}$ or $\frac{2}{3}$

Unit 1

2 A bag contains 57 blue marbles, 14 yellow marbles and 29 green marbles.

(a) Write down the number of yellow marbles as a fraction of the total number of marbles in the bag. Give your answer in its simplest form. **(2)**

(b) What percentage of marbles are not blue? **(1)**

(c) Circle a word from the list to describe the chance of each of the following events.

Think carefully about what these words mean

impossible   **unlikely**   **evens**   **likely**   **certain**

(i) A marble chosen at random from the bag is yellow. **(1)**

(ii) A marble chosen at random from the bag is not red. **(1)**

(a) $\dfrac{\text{Number of yellow marbles}}{\text{Total number of marbles}} = \dfrac{14}{100} = \dfrac{7}{50}$

(b) Percentage of marbles not blue = $\dfrac{43}{100} \times 100\% = 43\%$

(c) (i) Unlikely as there are only 14 yellow marbles out of 100.

(ii) Certain as none of the marbles are red.

Sample GCSE questions

3 Adam has two piles of cards (cards 1–4 and cards 5 to 9). He picks one card from each pile, multiplies the numbers on them, then records the answer in a table and replaces the cards.

(a) Complete this table to give all possible outcomes. **(3)**

	5	6	7	8	9
1	5	6	7	8	9
2	10				
3					27
4				32	36

(b) What is the probability of getting an answer less than 20? **(1)**

(c) On his school's charity day, Adam asks all 120 students in his year to pay 25p to choose cards as he has done. If they get an answer that is a multiple of 12, they get a prize of a tube of sweets costing 40p. Adam says he will be able to give more than £22 to his school's chosen charity. Is he correct? Explain your answer. **(4)**

(a)

	5	6	7	8	9
1	5	6	7	8	9
2	10	12	14	16	18
3	15	18	21	24	27
4	20	24	28	32	36

(b) P(answer less than 20) = $\frac{12}{20} = \frac{3}{5}$

(c) P(multiple of 12) = $\frac{4}{20} = \frac{1}{5}$

Number of students getting a multiple of 12 = $\frac{4}{20} \times 120 = 24$

Total amount of money taken = 120 × 25p = £30

Cost of prizes = 24 × 40p = £9.60

Amount of money Adam can give to charity = £30 − £9.60 = £20.40

Adam is incorrect.

Make sure your explanation is backed up by evidence

4 Ben organises the shuttle buses for a local hotel. The buses take guests to different venues. He records the length of the journey and the number of passengers over one week.

(a) Design a suitable data collection sheet for Ben to use for his observations. **(2)**

(b) Ben thinks that there will be positive correlation between the length of journey and the number of passengers. Explain why he may think this. **(1)**

Sample GCSE questions

(c) This scatter graph shows Ben's results for the week.

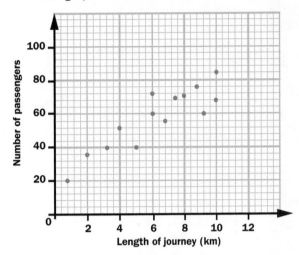

(i) How many passengers were on the bus for an 8km journey? **(1)**

(ii) How many passengers could be expected on the bus for an 11km journey? Show how you get your answer. **(1)**

(d) Does the data reflect Ben's thoughts on the correlation between the length of the journey and number of passengers? **(1)**

(a)

Length of journey (km)									
Number of passengers									

Any sensible reason should gain a mark

(b) People might decide to walk a short distance, but will definitely take the bus for a longer journey.

(c) (i)   70

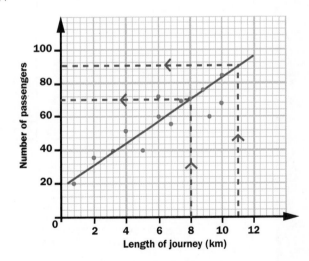

Draw the line of best fit through the middle of the set of points

Draw dotted lines to show how the answer is obtained

(ii) 90 (Line of best fit must be drawn to obtain this answer.)

(d) Yes. There is positive correlation.

Sample GCSE questions

Unit 1

5 The table shows the weight of 100 parcels sent from a delivery firm on one day.

Weight (kg)	Frequency
$0 < w \leqslant 5$	28
$5 < w \leqslant 8$	36
$8 < w \leqslant 10$	24
$10 < w \leqslant 20$	12

(a) Draw a fully labelled histogram to show the weights of the 100 parcels. **(3)**

(b) Estimate the probability that the first two parcels were over 8kg in weight. **(3)**

Check the class intervals →

(a)

Weight (kg)	Frequency	Class width	$\dfrac{\text{Frequency}}{\text{Class width}} = \dfrac{\text{Frequency}}{\text{density}}$
$0 < w \leqslant 5$	28	5	5.6
$5 < w \leqslant 8$	36	3	12
$8 < w \leqslant 10$	24	2	12
$10 < w \leqslant 20$	12	10	1.2

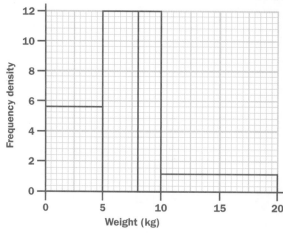

(b)   P(first parcel > 8kg) = $\dfrac{36}{100}$ = $\dfrac{9}{25}$

P(second parcel > 8kg) = $\dfrac{35}{99}$

P(first two parcels > 8kg) = $\dfrac{9}{25} \times \dfrac{35}{99}$ = $\dfrac{315}{2475}$ = $\dfrac{7}{55}$ or 0.127 to 3 d.p.

Exam practice questions

Unit 1 ① The dual bar chart shows sales of music downloads from an online music store. 🖩

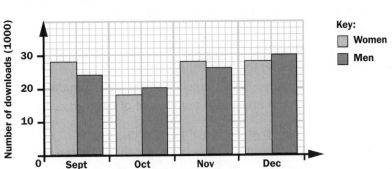

Key:
▢ Women
▢ Men

(a) Give a reason why sales were greatest in December. **(1)**

(b) The sales manager thinks that more men than women buy music downloads.
Does the data support this? Show working to justify your answers. **(3)**

Unit 1 ② Ten boys and ten girls are each given a French vocabulary test with 40 words.
Here is the number of correct answers for each girl.

24   36   24   38   18   40   22   18   36   24

The range of boys' scores is 24. The mean of boys' scores is 29.
Use the data to investigate the hypothesis:
'Girls are better than boys at learning French vocabulary.' **(5)**

Unit 1 ③ **(a)** The grades achieved by 50 music students in their piano exam were recorded in this table.
Calculate the mean grade. **(3)**

Grade	Number of students
1	1
2	2
3	10
4	18
5	15
6	4

(b) 25 other music students took exams in recorder and violin. Their grades are shown in this table.

		Recorder					
	Grade	1	2	3	4	5	Total
Violin	1	0	0	0	0	1	1
	2	0	3	0	2	0	5
	3	3	0	3	3	0	9
	4	2	2	2	2	0	8
	5	0	0	1	1	0	2
	Total	5	5	6	8	1	25

(i) What is the median grade for the violin exam? **(2)**

(ii) The head of music says her students seem to be better at violin than they are at recorder. Does the table suggest this? **(1)**

Exam practice questions

Unit 1 **4** What correlation would you expect in the following comparisons?

(a) The depth of mud on a sports field and the amount of rainfall. **(1)**

(b) The value of a car and its age. **(1)**

(c) The air temperature and the number of ice creams sold. **(1)**

(d) The length of a person's hair and the height they can jump. **(1)**

(e) The number of cups of tea poured from a teapot and the tea left in the teapot. **(1)**

(f) The number of people living in a house and the amount of electricity used. **(1)**

Unit 1 **5** A new CD is released from the group at the top of the charts.

A shop records the ages and number of people who bought the CD in the first hour of sale.

Age (a yrs)	$0 < a \leq 10$	$10 < a \leq 20$	$20 < a \leq 30$	$30 < a \leq 40$	$40 < a \leq 50$	$50 < a \leq 60$
Frequency	12	45	52	38	23	10

(a) Draw a frequency polygon for the information in the table. **(4)**

(b) Which is the modal class? **(1)**

(c) What is the mean age of the people who bought the CD? **(3)**

(d) In which class interval does the median age occur? **(2)**

(e) Comment on your results. **(1)**

Unit 1 **6** The dinner ladies in a school dining room ask all year 10 students about the drink they prefer to have with their lunch.

This pie chart gives the information they collected.

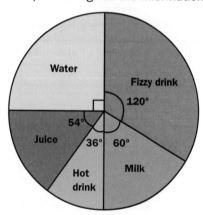

(a) Water was preferred by 40 students. How many students are in year 10? **(2)**

(b) How many students preferred a hot drink? **(2)**

(c) What percentage of students prefer milk with their lunch? **(2)**

(d) What fraction of students prefer juice with their lunch? **(2)**

(e) A student is selected at random.

   (i) What is the probability they prefer a fizzy drink? **(1)**

   (ii) What is the probability they prefer milk or a hot drink? **(1)**

Exam practice questions

Unit 1 **7** A Maths exam is sat by 100 students.
This table gives their marks.

Exam marks	Frequency	Cumulative frequency
0–10	0	0
11–20	3	3
21–30	4	7
31–40	20	
41–50	29	
51–60	25	
61–70	16	
71–80	3	

(a) Complete the cumulative frequency table. **(2)**

(b) Draw a cumulative frequency graph on this grid to illustrate the data in the table. **(4)**

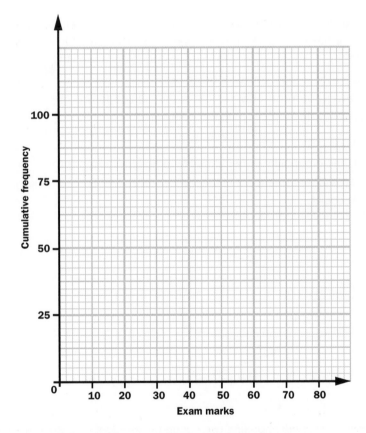

(c) The pass mark is 60%. How many students pass the exam? **(2)**

(d) Find the median mark and the inter-quartile range. **(3)**

(e) Draw a box plot to illustrate your answers to (d). **(2)**

(f) Comment on your box plot. **(1)**

Exam practice questions

Unit 1 **8** A Chinese take-away restaurant asks the local council for planning permission to open a new outlet in the middle of a housing estate.

(a) Suggest three questions that could be used in a survey of public opinion. **(3)**

(b) How would you make sure the survey was not biased? **(2)**

Unit 1 **9** Many of the customers of a newsagent's shop pay with coins.

By the end of one morning, the owner has a bag of coins that need to be sorted into separate packets for him to deposit into the bank.

The bag contains 24 × £2, 54 × £1, 92 × 50p, 140 × 20p, 80 × 10p, 40 × 5p, 200 × 2p and 150 × 1p coins. When he is sorting the coins, he picks them out at random from the bag.

(a) (i) How many coins has he got in the bag? **(1)**

(ii) What sum do they amount to? **(1)**

(b) Find the probability that the first coin he picks out is a...

(i) 20p coin **(1)**

(ii) £1 coin **(1)**

(iii) 1p or a 2p coin **(2)**

Unit 1 **10** An airport has four car parks. They are being renovated, so only one will be open at a time. The probability of North car park being open is 0.25. The probability of South car park being open is 0.35. The probability of East car park being open is 0.2.

(a) What is the probability of West car park being open? **(1)**

(b) What is the probability of North or South car parks being open? **(1)**

(c) What is the probability of West car park not being open? **(1)**

Unit 1 **11** Minnie goes to the library. She can borrow two library books at one time. They can be fiction or non-fiction. The probability of her choosing a fiction book is 0.68.

(a) Complete the tree diagram to show the different choices Minnie can make when choosing her two books. **(2)**

(b) Find the probability of Minnie choosing two fiction books. Give your answer to 3 s.f. **(2)**

(c) Find the probability of Minnie choosing at least one fiction book. Give your answer to 3 s.f. **(3)**

2 Number

The following topics are covered in this chapter:

- **Integers**
- **Powers and roots**
- **Fractions**
- **Decimals**
- **Percentages**
- **Ratio and proportion**
- **Approximations**
- **Calculator use**

2.1 Integers

LEARNING SUMMARY

After studying this section, you should be able to understand:

- order of operations
- positive and negative integers
- common factors and multiples
- prime numbers

Order of operations

Unit 1	✓
Unit 2	✓
Unit 3	✓

> You may not see BIDMAS on the exam paper but it is a good memory aid.

KEY POINT

Remember the order of working by using BIDMAS:

Brackets **I**ndices **D**ivision **M**ultiplication **A**ddition **S**ubtraction

(Sometimes you will see BODMAS. The O stands for orders, i.e. powers.)

Example

Work out $6^2 - 3(2 + 5)$

$$6^2 - 3(2 + 5) = 6^2 - 3(7)$$
$$= 6^2 - 21$$
$$= 36 - 21$$
$$= 15$$

Positive and negative integers

Unit 1	X
Unit 2	✓
Unit 3	X

Integers are whole numbers.

- Positive numbers are greater than zero (+).
- Negative numbers are less than zero (-).

Adding and subtracting integers

Integers can be shown on a number line.

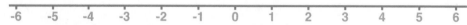

To add move right →
To subtract move left ←

Examples

(a) 2 + 3 = +5

(b) 2 – 6 = -4

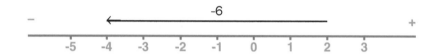

(c) 5 + (-2) = 3

(d) -3 – (-4) = 1

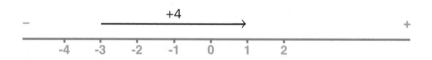

> Adding a negative number is the same as subtracting.
>
> If there is no sign, the integer is positive.

> Subtracting a negative number is the same as adding.

KEY POINT

When adding and subtracting integers, these rules can be used:
Same signs (+ +) or (– –) = +
Different signs (+ –) or (– +) = –

For example:
- 3 + (-6) = 3 – 6 = -3
- 50 – (-5) = 50 + 5 = +55

Multiplying and dividing integers

> Use the (+/–) or (–) calculator key to change the sign.

The rules for adding and subtracting integers also apply to multiplying and dividing, i.e. two like signs give a positive answer and two different signs give a negative answer.

For example:
- (-3) × (+6) = -18
- (-50) ÷ (-5) = +10

Common factors and multiples

Unit 1	X
Unit 2	✓
Unit 3	X

> **KEY POINT**
>
> A **factor** is a number that divides exactly into another number. It is a divisor.
> A **multiple** is a number that can be divided exactly by another number.

Some numbers have **common factors** and **common multiples**. For example:
- 8 is a factor of 24 (24 ÷ 8 = 3) and 40 (40 ÷ 8 = 5) so it is a common factor of both.
- 10 is a multiple of 2 (2 × 5 = 10), 5 (5 × 2 = 10), and 10 (10 × 1 = 10) so it is a **common multiple** of all of them.

> **KEY POINT**
>
> Highest Common Factor (**HCF**) is the highest factor common to two or more numbers.
>
> Least Common Multiple (**LCM**) is the lowest multiple common to two or more numbers.

For example:
- 30 has factors 1, 2, 3, 5, 6, 10, 15 and 30
  45 has factors 1, 3, 5, 9, 15 and 45
  ∴ 3, 5 and 15 are common factors of 30 and 45, but their HCF = 15

> The times table of a number is a list of its multiples.

- 7 has multiples 7, 14, 21, 28, 35, ...
  4 has multiples 4, 8, 12, 16, 20, 24, 28, 32, ...
  ∴ 28 is the lowest multiple common to 4 and 7, so their LCM = 28

Prime numbers

Unit 1	X
Unit 2	✓
Unit 3	X

> **KEY POINT**
>
> A **prime number** has only two factors, itself and 1. The only even prime number is 2. All other prime numbers are odd.

For example:
- 17 has factors 1 and 17 so it is a prime number.
- 15 has factors 1, 3, 5 and 15 so it is not a prime number.

> The factors of every integer include itself and 1.

> **KEY POINT**
>
> A factor that is a prime number is a **prime factor**. All positive integers can be shown to be the product of prime factors.

Example

Write 18 and 45 as products of their prime factors.
Then find the highest common factor and least common multiple of 18 and 45.

There are two methods of writing this down. It does not matter which you choose.

Method 1   Method 2

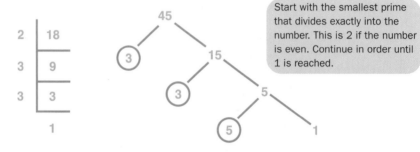

Start with the smallest prime that divides exactly into the number. This is 2 if the number is even. Continue in order until 1 is reached.

18 = 2 × 3 × 3   45 = 3 × 3 × 5

18 and 45 have factors 3 × 3 in common.
∴ highest common factor = 3 × 3 = 9
To find the least common multiple, you only need to count the common factors once, but all other factors must be included.
∴ least common multiple = 2 × 3 × 3 × 5 = 90

PROGRESS CHECK

Without using a calculator

1 Work out:
   (a) 4(6 − 3) − 3(8 ÷ 2)
   (b) 3(2 + 1) × 1 + 9

2 Work out:
   (a) 7 + (-3) − (-2)
   (b) -13 × -3
   (c) 36 ÷ 6
   (d) -156 ÷ 3

3 Write out the prime factors and find the highest common factor and least common multiple of:
   (a) 24 and 30
   (b) 45, 84 and 180

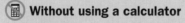

1. (a) 0 (b) 18 2. (a) 6 (b) 39 (c) 6 (d) -52 3. (a) 24 = 2 × 2 × 2 × 3, 30 = 2 × 3 × 5, highest common factor = 6, least common multiple = 120 (b) 45 = 3 × 3 × 5, 84 = 2 × 2 × 3 × 7, 180 = 2 × 2 × 3 × 3 × 5, highest common factor = 3, least common multiple = 1260

2.2 Powers and roots

LEARNING SUMMARY	After studying this section, you should be able to understand:
	• index notation
	• square roots and cube roots
	• index laws
	• standard index form

Index notation

Unit 1   X
Unit 2   ✓
Unit 3   X

KEY POINT

Using index or power notation is a shorthand way of writing numbers.

4^2 does not mean 4×2. Work out the value and you will see why!

For example:
- $4^2 = 4 \times 4$ [2 is the index]
  This is 4 squared or 4 to the power of 2.
- $4^3 = 4 \times 4 \times 4$ [3 is the index]
  This is 4 cubed or 4 to the power of 3.

Use the $\frac{1}{x}$ or x^{-1} calculator key to find the reciprocal of a number.

A negative index means that you use the reciprocal (divide the number into 1) and the index becomes positive.

For example:
- $7^{-3} = \frac{1}{7^3}$
- $5^{-4} = \frac{1}{5^4}$
- $\frac{1}{3^2} = 3^{-2}$

If the index is zero, the result is always 1. For example, $8^0 = 1$, $126^0 = 1$, $x^0 = 1$

Fractional and negative powers can be found on higher level papers.

A fraction index means a root. For example, $9^{\frac{1}{2}} = \sqrt{9}$, $27^{\frac{1}{3}} = \sqrt[3]{27}$, $p^{\frac{2}{5}} = \sqrt[5]{p^2}$

Square roots and cube roots

Unit 1   X
Unit 2   ✓
Unit 3   X

Square root ($\sqrt{\ }$)

KEY POINT

Taking the square root of a number is the opposite of squaring.

For example:
The square root of 25 ($\sqrt{25}$) is both +5 and -5 as $(+5)^2$ and $(-5)^2$ give 25.
Write this as $\sqrt{25} = \pm 5$

Cube root ($^3\sqrt{\ }$)

> **KEY POINT**
>
> Taking the **cube root** of a number is the opposite of cubing.

For example:

The cube root of 27 ($^3\sqrt{27}$) is +3 as $(+3)^3$ gives 27. Write this as $^3\sqrt{27} = 3$.
The cube root of 27 is not -3 as $(-3)^3$ gives -27.

> It helps if you can remember the squares of numbers up to 15 and the cubes of numbers up to 10, together with their square and cube roots.

Examples

Find:

(a) $\sqrt{36}$

$\sqrt{(6 \times 6)}$ and $\sqrt{-6 \times -6}$ so $\sqrt{36} = \pm 6$

(b) $^3\sqrt{125}$

$^3\sqrt{(5 \times 5 \times 5)} = 5$

Index laws

Unit 1	✗
Unit 2	✓
Unit 3	✗

You need to learn the following **index laws** or rules. The base integer has to be the same when index laws are applied.

- **Add powers when multiplying**
  $3^2 \times 3^5 = 3^{(2+5)} = 3^7$
  $x^3 \times x^2 \times x^4 = x^{(3+2+4)} = x^9$

- **Subtract powers when dividing**
  $6^3 \div 6 = 6^{(3-1)} = 6^2$
  $y^{10} \div y^3 = y^{(10-3)} = y^7$

  > If no power is given, it is assumed the index is 1 so $6 = 6^1$

> If a question asks for a value, do not leave it in index form.

- **Multiply powers when raising one power to another power**
  $(4^2)^3 = 4^{(2 \times 3)} = 4^6$
  $(n^4)^5 = n^{(4 \times 5)} = n^{20}$

> Work with numbers and letters separately if they are in the same expression.
> For example
> $2a^3 \times 5a^2 = 10a^5$

Examples

Work out:

(a) $5^2 \times 5$
  $= 5^{(2+1)} = 5^3 = 5 \times 5 \times 5 = 125$

(b) $10^5 \div 10^4$
  $= 10^{(5-4)} = 10^1 = 10$

(c) $(3^2)^3$
  $= 3^{(2 \times 3)} = 3^6 = 3 \times 3 \times 3 \times 3 \times 3 \times 3 = 729$

Standard index form

Unit 1	✓
Unit 2	✓
Unit 3	✗

For standard index form on a calculator, see page 77.

Standard index form can be found on higher level papers.

KEY POINT

Standard index form is a shorthand way of writing very large or very small numbers. This is done by converting them into the form $a \times 10^n$ where a is any number between 1 and 10 and n is a power of 10.

Examples

1. Write in standard index form:
   (a) $2\,600\,000 = 26 \times 100\,000$
   $$= 2.6 \times 10^6$$

   (b) $0.000\,000\,0735 = 735 \div 10^{10}$
   $$= 735 \times 10^{-10}$$
   $$= 7.35 \times 10^{-8}$$

2. Write the following as ordinary numbers:
   (a) $1.72 \times 10^7 = 1.72 \times 10 \times 10 \times 10 \times 10 \times 10 \times 10 \times 10$
   $$= 17\,200\,000$$

   (b) $3.21 \times 10^{-8} = 3.21 \div 10^8$
   $$= 0.000\,000\,0321$$

3. Write the answer in standard index form:
   $$\frac{7 \times 10^3 \times 10^{-1} \times 6.1 \times 10^6}{2 \times 10^4}$$
   $$= \frac{(7 \times 6.1) \times (10^3 \times 10^{-1} \times 10^6)}{2 \times 10^4}$$
   $$= \frac{42.7 \times 10^8}{2 \times 10^4}$$
   $$= 21.35 \times 10^4$$
   $$= 2.135 \times 10^5$$

Collect together numbers and powers of 10 and work them out separately.

PROGRESS CHECK

Without using a calculator

1. Simplify and leave your answer in index form:
   (a) $(3^{-2})^3$ **(b)** $8^5 \div 8^3$ **(c)** $3a^5 \times 5a^3 \times a$ **(d)** $(n^6)^{\frac{1}{4}}$

2. Find the value of:
   (a) 4×5^0 **(b)** $4^2 \times 4^4$ **(c)** 6^{-2} **(d)** $(5^6)^{\frac{1}{2}}$

3. Write these in standard index form:
   (a) $0.003\,15$
   (b) $5\,217\,000$
   (c) $\dfrac{1}{\sqrt{64}}$
   (d) $(1.35 \times 10^{-3}) \div (5 \times 10^{-5})$

3. (a) 3.15×10^{-3} (b) 5.217×10^6 (c) 1.25×10^{-1} (d) 2.7×10
2. (a) 4 (b) 4096 (c) 0.028 (d) 125
1. (a) 3^{-6} (b) 8^2 (c) $15a^9$ (d) $n^{\frac{3}{2}}$

2.3 Fractions

LEARNING SUMMARY

After studying this section, you should be able to understand:
- equivalent fractions
- improper fractions and mixed numbers
- working with fractions

Equivalent fractions

Unit 1 ✓
Unit 2 ✓
Unit 3 ✓

KEY POINT

Equivalent fractions have equal value, but different form.

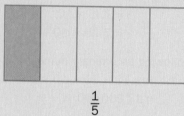

$$\frac{1}{5} \qquad = \qquad \frac{2}{10}$$

To find equivalent fractions, multiply or divide the top number (**numerator**) and the bottom number (**denominator**) by the same factor.

For example:

$$\frac{3 \times 2}{5 \times 2} = \frac{6}{10}$$

$$\frac{20 \div 5}{25 \div 5} = \frac{4}{5}$$

KEY POINT

Dividing by a common factor is called cancelling to lowest terms.

It is quicker to cancel by the highest common factor, but you should reach the same answer if you cancel in stages.

For example:

$$\frac{60 \div 4}{128 \div 4} = \frac{15}{32} \quad \longleftarrow \boxed{\text{HCF} = 4}$$

but

$$\frac{60 \div 2}{128 \div 2} = \frac{30 \div 2}{64 \div 2} = \frac{15}{32} \quad \longleftarrow \boxed{\begin{array}{l}\text{Cancel by 2 first and then} \\ \text{cancel by 2 again}\end{array}}$$

Examples

1. Simplify $\frac{360}{480}$ into its lowest terms:

$$\frac{360}{480} \div 10 = \frac{36}{48} \div 12 = \frac{3}{4}$$

> The HCF of 360 and 480 = 120 but it is easier to cancel by 10 first

2. Use equivalent fractions to put these fractions in order, starting with the lowest:

$$\frac{4}{5}, \frac{1}{60}, \frac{7}{12}, \frac{6}{15}, \frac{2}{3}$$

The lowest denominator common to all of the fractions = 60. Multiply the denominators by a factor to give 60 in each case.

$$\frac{4}{5} \times \frac{12}{12} = \frac{48}{60}$$

$$\frac{1}{60} \times \frac{1}{1} = \frac{1}{60}$$

$$\frac{7}{12} \times \frac{5}{5} = \frac{35}{60}$$

$$\frac{6}{15} \times \frac{4}{4} = \frac{24}{60}$$

$$\frac{2}{3} \times \frac{20}{20} = \frac{40}{60}$$

In order from the lowest: $\frac{1}{60}, \frac{24}{60}, \frac{35}{60}, \frac{40}{60}, \frac{48}{60}$

Always give the answer in the original terms: $\frac{1}{60}, \frac{6}{15}, \frac{7}{12}, \frac{2}{3}, \frac{4}{5}$

> Remember that the numerator and denominator must be multiplied by the same factor.

Improper fractions and mixed numbers

Unit 1 ✓
Unit 2 ✓
Unit 3 ✓

KEY POINT

An **improper fraction** has a numerator larger than the denominator.
For example: $\frac{11}{3}, \frac{15}{4}, \frac{17}{2}$

A **mixed number** (or **mixed fraction**) consists of a whole number with a fraction.
For example: $1\frac{2}{7}, 4\frac{1}{5}, 6\frac{2}{3}$

Improper fractions can be converted into mixed numbers by dividing the numerator by the denominator.

For example:

$$\frac{11}{3} = 3 \text{ (remainder 2)} = 3\frac{2}{3}$$

Mixed numbers can be converted into improper fractions. Multiply the whole number by the denominator, add it to the numerator and put the total over the denominator.

For example:

$$1\frac{2}{7} = \frac{(1 \times 7) + 2}{7} = \frac{9}{7}$$

Working with fractions

Unit 1 ✓
Unit 2 ✓
Unit 3 ✓

Adding and subtracting fractions

KEY POINT

To add or subtract fractions, first find the lowest denominator common to all (their LCM) and convert to equivalent fractions.

- Adding fractions:

$$\frac{2}{3} + \frac{1}{6}$$

$$= \frac{4}{6} + \frac{1}{6} = \frac{5}{6}$$

LCM = 6 so multiply the numerator and denominator in $\frac{2}{3}$ by 2 to get the equivalent fraction

You must not add numerators and denominators.
$$\frac{2}{3} + \frac{1}{6} \neq \frac{3}{9}$$

- Subtracting fractions:

$$\frac{4}{5} - \frac{3}{10}$$

$$= \frac{8}{10} - \frac{3}{10} = \frac{5}{10} = \frac{1}{2}$$

LCM = 10 so multiply the numerator and denominator in $\frac{4}{5}$ by 2 to get the equivalent fraction

Give answer in lowest terms, so cancel by 5

Adding and subtracting mixed numbers

Examples

Find:

(a) $2\frac{4}{7} + 1\frac{1}{5}$

$$= 3 + \left(\frac{4}{7}\frac{\times 5}{\times 5} + \frac{1}{5}\frac{\times 7}{\times 7}\right) = 3 + \left(\frac{20}{35} + \frac{7}{35}\right) = 3\frac{27}{35}$$

LCM = 35

To avoid making mistakes when subtracting, change mixed numbers to improper fractions first.

(b) $4\frac{2}{3} - 2\frac{3}{4}$

$$= \frac{14}{3} - \frac{11}{4}$$

$$= \frac{14}{3}\frac{\times 4}{\times 4} - \frac{11}{4}\frac{\times 3}{\times 3} = \frac{56}{12} - \frac{33}{12}$$

$$= \frac{23}{12}$$

LCM = 12

$$= 1\frac{11}{12}$$

You can do the calculation without changing to improper fractions first but make sure you work through the calculation carefully.

(c) $3\frac{7}{10} - 2\frac{1}{4}$

$$= 1 + \left(\frac{7}{10}\frac{\times 2}{\times 2} - \frac{1}{4}\frac{\times 5}{\times 5}\right) = 1 + \left(\frac{14}{20} - \frac{5}{20}\right) = 1\frac{9}{20}$$

LCM = 20

Multiplying fractions

KEY POINT

To multiply two fractions, multiply the numerators and multiply the denominators. You may cancel first if there are common factors, otherwise cancel at the end.

Examples

Find:

(a) $\dfrac{3}{5} \times \dfrac{2}{7}$

$= \dfrac{3 \times 2}{5 \times 7} = \dfrac{6}{35}$

(b) $\dfrac{6}{7} \times \dfrac{14}{25}$

$= \dfrac{6 \times 14}{7 \times 25}$

$= \dfrac{6 \times \cancel{14}^{2}}{\cancel{7}_{1} \times 25} = \dfrac{12}{25}$ ← Cancel by 7

Dividing fractions

Division is the opposite or inverse of multiplication.

For example, if you divide by 5 the result is the same as multiplying by $\dfrac{1}{5}$

$25 \div 5 = 5 \qquad 25 \times \dfrac{1}{5} = \dfrac{25}{5} = 5$

KEY POINT

Dividing by a fraction gives the same result as multiplying by its reciprocal.

Examples

Find:

> All integers can be written over 1 to form a fraction.

(a) $\dfrac{2}{7} \div \dfrac{1}{3}$

$= \dfrac{2}{7} \times \dfrac{3}{1}$ ← Turn divisor upside down and multiply

$= \dfrac{6}{7}$

(b) $1\dfrac{4}{5} \div 2\dfrac{1}{3}$

> Always change mixed numbers to improper fractions before multiplying or dividing.

$= \dfrac{9}{5} \div \dfrac{7}{3}$

$= \dfrac{9}{5} \times \dfrac{3}{7}$

$= \dfrac{27}{35}$

PROGRESS CHECK

🖩 **Without using a calculator**

1. Write these fractions in their lowest terms:

   (a) $\dfrac{32}{64}$ (b) $\dfrac{6}{9}$ (c) $\dfrac{44}{55}$ (d) $\dfrac{26}{48}$

2. Work out:

   (a) $\dfrac{8}{25} + \dfrac{3}{5}$ (b) $\dfrac{5}{8} - \dfrac{1}{6}$ (c) $1\dfrac{3}{4} + 4\dfrac{2}{3}$ (d) $6\dfrac{1}{7} - \dfrac{3}{14}$

3. Work out:

   (a) $\dfrac{2}{15} \times 3$ (b) $\dfrac{3}{7} \div \dfrac{3}{5}$ (c) $3\dfrac{2}{5} \times 1\dfrac{1}{4}$ (d) $1\dfrac{3}{4} \div \dfrac{5}{8}$

1. (a) $\dfrac{1}{2}$ (b) $\dfrac{2}{3}$ (c) $\dfrac{4}{5}$ (d) $\dfrac{13}{24}$ 2. (a) $\dfrac{23}{25}$ (b) $\dfrac{11}{24}$ (c) $6\dfrac{5}{12}$ (d) $5\dfrac{13}{14}$ 3. (a) $\dfrac{2}{5}$ (b) $\dfrac{5}{7}$ (c) $4\dfrac{1}{4}$ (d) $2\dfrac{4}{5}$

2.4 Decimals

LEARNING SUMMARY	After studying this section, you should be able to understand: • place value • working with decimals • converting fractions to decimals • converting decimals to fractions

Place value

Unit 1	✓
Unit 2	✓
Unit 3	✓

Decimals are numbers based on 10. They consist of an integer followed by a decimal point and a decimal fraction.

Integer ⟶ **102.35** ⟵ Decimal fraction

Decimal point

KEY POINT

The **place value** of each digit depends on its position in reference to the decimal point. Decimal place is usually shortened to d.p.

1000s	100s	10s	1s		$\frac{1}{10s}$	$\frac{1}{100s}$	$\frac{1}{1000s}$
1	3	2	5	.	2	3	4

As the places move to the right from the decimal point, they are divided by 10. As the places move to the left from the decimal point, they are multiplied by 10.

Examples

1. Give the value of the underlined digits:
   - **(a)** 10.5̲21
     5 is in the $\frac{1}{10}$ place and equals $\frac{5}{10}$
   - **(b)** 3.04̲9̲
     9 is in the $\frac{1}{1000}$ place and equals $\frac{9}{1000}$
   - **(c)** 0.0007̲
     7 is in the $\frac{1}{10\,000}$ place and equals $\frac{7}{10\,000}$

2. Put these decimals in order of size starting with the smallest:
   2.273   2.05   2.275   2.068   2.108
   The integers before the decimal point are the same.
   Two of the decimals (2.05, 2.068) have 0 in the $\frac{1}{10}$ place so these are smaller than the other three decimals.
   2.05 is smaller than 2.068 because of the digits in the $\frac{1}{100}$ place.
   2.108 is the next decimal as it has 1 in the $\frac{1}{10}$ place.
   2.273 is smaller than 2.275 because of the digits in the $\frac{1}{1000}$ place.
   The correct order is: 2.05   2.068   2.108   2.273   2.275

Compare each place in each decimal in turn.

Working with decimals

Adding and subtracting decimals

KEY POINT

When adding or subtracting decimals, line up the decimal points. This makes sure the place values are correct.

Examples

Work out:

(a)   6.36 + 42.73

$$\begin{array}{r} 6.36 \\ +\ 42.73 \\ \hline 49.09 \\ \tiny 1 \end{array}$$

(b)   37.83 − 5.21

$$\begin{array}{r} 37.83 \\ -\ 5.21 \\ \hline 32.62 \end{array}$$

Multiplying decimals

KEY POINT

When multiplying decimals, ignore the decimal points. Count the total decimal places in the numbers being multiplied and give the answer to the same total of decimal places.

Examples

Work out:

(a) 1.35×0.2 — Total d.p. = 3

$135 \times 2 = 270$ — Multiply ignoring the decimal points.

$\therefore 1.35 \times 0.2 = 0.27$ — Move the digits three places to the right as there are 3 d.p. in the question. You do not need to show the final zero.

(b) 0.3×0.2

$3 \times 2 = 6$ — Total d.p. = 2

$\therefore 0.3 \times 0.2 = 0.06$ — Move the digits two places to the right as there are 2 d.p. in the question. The zero in the $\frac{1}{10}$ place must be shown so that 6 is in the $\frac{1}{100}$ place.

(c) 23.6×1.3

$$\begin{array}{r} 236 \\ \times\ \ \ 13 \\ \hline 708 \\ \tiny 1\ 1 \\ 2360 \\ \hline 3068 \\ \tiny 1 \end{array}$$

$\therefore 23.6 \times 1.3 = 30.68$

Dividing decimals

> **KEY POINT**
>
> When dividing decimals, multiply the divisor (the number doing the dividing) by a power of ten to make it a whole number. Multiply the dividend (the number being divided) by the same power of ten. There is no need to alter the d.p. in the answer.

Examples

Work out:

(a) $0.98 \div 0.7$

$= 9.8 \div 7$ ← Multiply 0.7 by 10 to make it a whole number, then multiply 0.98 by 10

$= 1.4$

(b) $1.368 \div 0.04$

$= 136.8 \div 4$ ← Multiply 0.04 by 100 to make it a whole number, then multiply 1.368 by 100

$= 34.2$

(c) $23.04 \div 3$ ← It is only necessary to multiply the divisor if it is a decimal

$= 7.68$

Converting fractions to decimals

Unit 1 ✓
Unit 2 ✓
Unit 3 ✓

> **KEY POINT**
>
> To convert a fraction to a decimal divide the numerator by the denominator.

It is useful to remember the decimal conversions of some common fractions such as:

$\frac{1}{2} = 0.5$ $\frac{1}{4} = 0.25$ $\frac{1}{5} = 0.2$ $\frac{1}{10} = 0.1$ $\frac{1}{8} = 0.125$

- A decimal that ends is called a **terminating decimal**. For example:

$\frac{2}{5} = 2 \div 5 = 0.4$

- A decimal that does not end, but where some numbers repeat, is called a **recurring decimal**. For example:

$\frac{1}{3} = 1 \div 3 = 0.333\,333\,33...$

$\frac{3}{11} = 3 \div 11 = 0.272\,727\,2727...$

$\frac{2}{7} = 2 \div 7 = 0.285\,714\,285\,714\,285\,714...$

A shorthand way of writing a recurring decimal is to use dots to indicate the repeating pattern. For example:

$0.333\,333\,33... = 0.\dot{3}$

$0.272\,727\,2727... = 0.\dot{2}\dot{7}$

$0.285\,714\,285\,714\,285\,714... = 0.\dot{2}85\,71\dot{4}$

Converting decimals to fractions

Unit 1 ✓
Unit 2 ✓
Unit 3 ✓

All terminating decimals can be written as a fraction with an integer as the numerator and denominator. Use place value to change a decimal to a fraction.

Examples

Write as fractions:

(a) $0.9 = \dfrac{9}{10}$

(b) $0.07 = \dfrac{7}{100}$

(c) $0.39 = \dfrac{3}{10} + \dfrac{9}{100}$

$= \dfrac{30}{100} + \dfrac{9}{100}$ ← $\dfrac{3}{10}$ is equivalent to $\dfrac{30}{100}$

$= \dfrac{39}{100}$

(d) $0.763 = \dfrac{7}{10} + \dfrac{6}{100} + \dfrac{3}{1000}$

$= \dfrac{700}{1000} + \dfrac{60}{1000} + \dfrac{3}{1000}$ ← Use equivalent fractions again

$= \dfrac{763}{1000}$

Recurring decimals are converted to fractions using the method described below.

Examples

1. Write $0.\dot{3}$ as a fraction.

$0.\dot{3} = 0.333\,333\,333...$ **a**

$0.\dot{3} \times 10 = 3.333\,333\,333...$ **b**

Multiply by 10^n where n is the total repeating digits

b − **a** = 3 ← Subtracting eliminates the recurring digits

This means that $0.\dot{3} \times 9 = 3$

∴ $0.\dot{3} = \dfrac{3}{9} = \dfrac{1}{3}$

2. Write $0.\dot{2}\dot{7}$ as a fraction.

$0.\dot{2}\dot{7} = 0.272\,727\,272\,727...$ **a**

$0.\dot{2}\dot{7} \times 100 = 27.272\,727\,2727...$ **b** ←

There are two repeating digits so multiply by 100

b − **a** = 27 ← Subtracting eliminates the recurring digits

This means that $0.\dot{2}\dot{7} \times 99 = 27$

∴ $0.\dot{2}\dot{7} = \dfrac{27}{99} = \dfrac{3}{11}$

3. Write $0.\dot{2}85\,71\dot{4}$ as a fraction.

$0.\dot{2}85\,71\dot{4} = 0.285\,714\,285\,714\,285\,714...$ **a**

$0.\dot{2}85\,71\dot{4} \times 10^6 = 285\,714.285\,714\,285\,714...$ **b**

b − **a** = 285 714

This means that $0.\dot{2}85\,71\dot{4} \times 999\,999 = 285\,714$

∴ $0.\dot{2}85\,71\dot{4} = \dfrac{285\,714}{999\,999} = \dfrac{2}{7}$

If you have a fraction key [$a^b/_c$] on your calculator, you may want to use it here to put the fraction in its lowest terms.

1 Work out:

(a) $201.5 + 0.206$ (b) $5.26 - 0.4$ (c) 4.2×0.01 (d) $27.3 \div 0.03$

2 Change these fractions to decimals:

(a) $\frac{7}{25}$ (b) $\frac{3}{8}$ (c) $\frac{4}{9}$ (d) $\frac{19}{33}$

3 Give these decimals as fractions in their lowest terms:

(a) 0.404 (b) 0.66 (c) 0.275 (d) $0.\dot{2}1\dot{6}$

3. (a) $\frac{101}{250}$ (b) $\frac{33}{50}$ (c) $\frac{11}{40}$ (d) $\frac{8}{37}$

1. (a) 201.706 (b) 4.86 (c) 0.042 (d) 910 2. (a) 0.28 (b) 0.375 (c) $0.\dot{4}$ (d) $0.\dot{5}\dot{7}$

2.5 Percentages

After studying this section, you should be able to understand:

- conversion of fractions, decimals and percentages
- percentage of a quantity
- one quantity as a percentage of another
- percentage change
- reversed percentages
- simple and compound interest

Conversion of fractions, decimals and percentages

Unit 1 ✓
Unit 2 ✓
Unit 3 ✓

Percentages and fractions

A fraction with a denominator of 100 is a **percentage** (%).

For example:

- $\frac{11}{100} = 11\%$  This means 11 parts per 100

- $\frac{27}{100} = 27\%$

To change a percentage to a fraction, write the percentage over 100.
Always give the fraction in its lowest terms.

Examples

Change to fractions:

(a) $9\% = \frac{9}{100}$

(b) $15\% = \frac{15}{100} = \frac{3}{20}$ Cancel by 5 to lowest terms

It is useful to remember the following percentages and fractions:

$1\% = \dfrac{1}{100}$ $5\% = \dfrac{1}{20}$ $10\% = \dfrac{1}{10}$ $20\% = \dfrac{1}{5}$

$25\% = \dfrac{1}{4}$ $33\frac{1}{3}\% = \dfrac{1}{3}$ $50\% = \dfrac{1}{2}$ $75\% = \dfrac{3}{4}$

KEY POINT

To change a fraction to a percentage, multiply by 100%.

Examples

Change to percentages:

(a) $\dfrac{3}{4} = \dfrac{3}{4} \times 100\% = \dfrac{300}{4} = 75\%$

(b) $\dfrac{2}{3} = \dfrac{2}{3} \times 100\% = \dfrac{200}{3} = 66\frac{2}{3}\%$

Percentages and decimals

KEY POINT

To change a percentage to a decimal, divide by 100.

Examples

Change to decimals:

(a) $63\% = \dfrac{63}{100} = 0.63$

(b) $35\% = \dfrac{35}{100} = 0.35$

(c) $8\% = \dfrac{8}{100} = 0.08$

Dividing by a power of 10 appears to move the decimal point to the left by the number of zeros.

KEY POINT

To change a decimal to a percentage, multiply by 100%.

Examples

Change to percentages:

(a) $0.43 = 0.43 \times 100\% = 43\%$

(b) $0.7 = 0.7 \times 100\% = 70\%$

(c) $0.006 = 0.006 \times 100\% = 0.6\%$

Multiplying by a power of 10 appears to move the decimal point to the right by the number of zeros.

Percentage of a quantity

Unit 1   ✓
Unit 2   ✓
Unit 3   ✗

KEY POINT

To find a percentage of a quantity, write the percentage over 100 and multiply by the quantity.

VAT stands for Value Added Tax. The percentage charged changes from time to time and country to country.

Examples

1. Find 20% of £200.

   $$\frac{20}{100} \times £200^{2} = 20 \times £2 \quad \leftarrow \boxed{\text{Cancel by 100}}$$
   $$= £40$$

2. Find the VAT charged at 17.5% on a washing machine costing £398.

   $$VAT = \frac{17.5}{100} \times £398 = \frac{£6965}{100}$$
   $$= £69.65$$

One quantity as a percentage of another

Unit 1   ✓
Unit 2   ✓
Unit 3   ✗

KEY POINT

To write one quantity as a percentage of another, divide the first quantity by the second quantity and multiply by 100%.

Examples

1. Find 45 as percentage of 180.

   $$\frac{45}{180} \times 100\% \quad \leftarrow \boxed{\text{Cancel by 20}}$$

   $$= \frac{45 \times 5}{9} \quad \leftarrow \boxed{\text{Cancel by 9}}$$

   $$= \frac{5 \times 5}{1}$$

   $$= \frac{25}{1} = 25\%$$

2. Express 150m as a percentage of 120km.

   $$\frac{150m}{120km} \times 100\%$$

   $$= \frac{150}{120\,000} \times 100 \quad \leftarrow \boxed{1000m = 1km}$$

   $$= \frac{15}{120} = 0.125\% \ (\text{or } \tfrac{1}{8}\%) \quad \leftarrow \boxed{\text{Cancel by } 10^3}$$

Always make sure both quantities are in the same units.

3. Express 8 hours as a percentage of a day.

   $$\frac{8hrs}{1 \ day} \times 100\%$$

   $$= \frac{8}{24} \times 100 \quad \leftarrow \boxed{24hrs \ in \ a \ day}$$

   $$= \frac{1}{3} \times 100$$

   $$= \frac{100}{3} = 33\tfrac{1}{3}\%$$

Percentage change

Unit 1 ✓
Unit 2 ✓
Unit 3 ✗

Percentages are used in many real-life situations. Any of the following words for percentage increase and percentage decrease may be used:

- Percentage increase – gain, profit, inflation, surcharge, appreciation
- Percentage decrease – reduction, discount, loss, depreciation

To find the percentage change, multiply the original amount by a multiplier.

> You may be asked to find the percentage increase or decrease. Sometimes you will be asked for a final amount. Always read the question carefully.

KEY POINT

If there is a percentage increase, multiply by:
(1 + the percentage as a decimal)
If there is a percentage decrease, multiply by:
(1 – the percentage as a decimal)

Examples

> Another method is to find the value of the increase (or decrease) and add (or subtract) it to find the final amount. This takes longer and errors may be introduced.

1. A chair costs £150 plus 17.5% VAT. What is the total price?
   Multiplier $= 1 + \dfrac{17.5}{100} = 1 + 0.175 = 1.175$ ← + because of increase
   Total cost $= £150 \times 1.175 = £176.25$

2. A TV costing £650 is discounted by 10%. What is the sale price?
   Multiplier $= 1 - \dfrac{10}{100} = 1 - 0.1 = 0.9$ ← – because of decrease
   Sale price $= £650 \times 0.9 = £585$

Reversed percentages

Unit 1 ✓
Unit 2 ✓
Unit 3 ✗

Sometimes you will be given an increased (or decreased) amount and asked to find the original quantity. To find the value before a percentage change, divide the original amount by a multiplier.

KEY POINT

To find the value before a percentage increase, divide by:
(1 + the percentage as a decimal)
To find the value before a percentage decrease, divide by:
(1 – the percentage as a decimal)

> Reversed percentages can be found on higher level papers.

Examples

1. Adam gets a 3% rise in his salary. His new salary is £450 a month. What was his salary before the rise?
   Multiplier $= 1 + \dfrac{3}{100} = 1 + 0.03 = 1.03$ ← + because of increase
   Original salary $= £450 \div 1.03 = £436.89$

2. Kizzy's bicycle costs £125 in a sale. The discount was 15%. What was the original cost?
   Multiplier $= 1 - \dfrac{15}{100} = 1 - 0.15 = 0.85$ ← – because of decrease
   Original cost $= £125 \div 0.85 = £147.06$

> Always check that your answer makes sense!

Simple and compound interest

Unit 1 ✓
Unit 2 ✗
Unit 3 ✗

KEY POINT

Interest is paid on money invested as savings or borrowed as a loan.

Simple interest

KEY POINT

Simple interest is paid each year. It is not added to the original amount when the following year's interest is calculated.

Simple interest = invested or borrowed amount × time invested or borrowed in years × rate of interest as a decimal

Example

Find the simple interest on £1400 for 4 years at 3% per year.

Simple interest = £1400 × 4 × 0.03 = £168

Amount | Time | Interest as decimal

Compound interest

Compound interest can be found on higher level papers.

KEY POINT

Compound interest is calculated on the amount invested or borrowed plus the interest added each year.

Example

£5000 is invested for 3 years at a compound interest of 3% per year. Work out the total compound interest earned.

1st year: Investment = £5000
Interest = £5000 x 0.03 = £150   0.03 is 3% as a decimal
Total after 1 year = £5150

2nd year: Investment = £5150
Interest = £5150 x 0.03 = £154.50
Total after 2 years = £5304.50

3rd year: Investment = £5304.50
Interest = £5304.50 x 0.03 = £159.14
Total after 3 years = £5463.64

Total compound interest = final total – original investment
= £5463.64 – £5000
= £463.64

See page 78 for repeated percentage increase.

KEY POINT

Instead of working through repeated calculations, compound interest can be calculated by using the following equation:

Final total = original amount (1 + rate of interest as a decimal)^n
(n is the number of periods of investment time)
You can then calculate the total interest.

Example

£5000 is invested for 3 years at a compound interest of 3% per year. Work out the total compound interest earned.

Final total = original amount (1 + rate of interest as a decimal)^n
$$= £5000(1 + 0.03)^3$$
$$= £5000 \times 1.03^3$$
$$= £5463.64$$

Total compound interest = final total − original investment
$$= £5463.64 − £5000$$
$$= £463.64$$

PROGRESS CHECK

1. Change to fractions:
   (a) 17%   **(b)** 36%   **(c)** 15%   **(d)** 38%

2. Change to decimals:
   (a) 18%   **(b)** 9%   **(c)** 77%   **(d)** 32.5%

3. Change to percentages:
   (a) $\frac{5}{8}$ **(b)** $\frac{13}{15}$ **(c)** 0.72   **(d)** 0.0425

4. Find:
   (a) 2.5% of £1500
   (b) 40% of 2km
   (c) 0.75% of 5000

5. Find:
   (a) 18 as a percentage of 90   **(b)** 60p as a percentage of £1
   (c) 45mins as a percentage of 3hrs

6. Increase:
   (a) £35 by 20%   **(b)** £55 by 65%   **(c)** £4200 by 5%

7. Decrease:
   (a) £108 by 25%   **(b)** £456 by 14%   **(c)** £3.50 by 30%

8. Find the original amount:
   (a) What was increased by 5% to give £189.75?
   (b) What was increased by 15% to give £324.30?
   (c) What was decreased by 40% to give £40.60?
   (d) What was decreased by 1.5% to give £81.90?

9. **(a)** Find the simple interest on £1250 at 3% interest per year after 6 months.
   (b) A man borrowed £4500 for 2 years at 4% compound interest. How much is owed after 2 years?

1. (a) $\frac{17}{100}$ (b) $\frac{9}{25}$ (c) $\frac{3}{20}$ (d) $\frac{19}{50}$ 2. (a) 0.18 (b) 0.09 (c) 0.77 (d) 0.325 3. (a) 62.5% (b) 86$\frac{2}{3}$% (c) 72% (d) 4.25% 4. (a) £37.50 (b) 800m (c) 37.5 5. (a) 20% (b) 60% (c) 25% 6. (a) £42 (b) £90.75 (c) £4410 7. (a) £81 (b) £392.16 (c) £2.45 8. (a) £180.71 (b) £282 (c) £67.67 (d) £83.15 9. (a) £18.75 (b) £4867.20

2.6 Ratio and proportion

LEARNING SUMMARY

After studying this section, you should be able to understand:

- simplifying ratios
- dividing a quantity in a given ratio
- proportion

Simplifying ratios

Unit 1 ✓
Unit 2 ✓
Unit 3 ✓

KEY POINT

Ratios are used to compare quantities. They should be treated in a similar way to fractions. A colon is used to denote a ratio, e.g. 2 : 3 or 3 : 5 : 7

For example:

A bag contains 6 red balls and 3 black balls.

Ratio of red : black = 6 : 3

A ratio can be simplified or given in its lowest terms by dividing all parts by their highest common factor.

In the example above, the HCF is 3 so divide both numbers in the ratio by 3

Ratio of red : black = $\div 3 \overset{6\,:\,3}{\underset{2\,:\,1}{}} \div 3$

KEY POINT

Make sure all parts of the ratio are measured in the same units.

Examples

Simplify these ratios giving them in their lowest terms:

(a) 125g : 250g

= 1 : 2 ←   HCF = 125

(b) 64p : £1

= 64 : 100 ←   Change £ to p

= 16 : 25 ←   HCF = 4

(c) 0.75km : 300m : 1.25km

= 750 : 300 : 1250 ←   Change km to m

= 15 : 6 : 25 ←   HCF = 50

KEY POINT

Ratios may sometimes be given in the form 1 : n where n represents a number. This is used to write scales for maps.

Examples

1. Write the ratio 5 : 6 in the form 1 : n

   $$5 : 6 = \frac{5}{5} : \frac{6}{5}$$ ← Divide both parts of the ratio by the first amount

   $$= 1 : 1\frac{1}{5}$$
   $$= 1 : 1.2$$

2. On a map 2cm represents 1km. Write this scale in the form 1 : n

   Scale = 2cm : 1km
   = 2cm : 1000m ← Change km to m
   Change m to cm
   = 2cm : 100 000cm ←
   = 1 : 50 000 ← Divide both sides of the ratio by 2

Dividing a quantity in a given ratio

Unit 1   X
Unit 2   ✓
Unit 3   X

KEY POINT

To divide a quantity in a given ratio, first find the total number of parts.
Divide the quantity by this total, to give the value of a single share.
Multiply each part of the ratio by the value of the single share.

Examples

1. Divide 120 in the ratio 5 : 3

   Total number of shares = 5 + 3 = 8
   Value of one share = 120 ÷ 8 = 15
   Value of five shares = 5 × 15 = 75
   Value of three shares = 3 × 15 = 45
   ∴ 120 divided in the ratio 5 : 3 = 75 : 45

2. A grandmother leaves £21 000 in her will to be shared by her four
   grandchildren in the ratio 3 : 5 : 4 : 2. How much will each
   grandchild receive?

   Total number of shares = 3 + 5 + 4 + 2 = 14
   Value of one share = £21 000 ÷ 14 = £1500
   Value of three shares = £1500 × 3 = £4500
   Value of five shares = £1500 × 5 = £7500
   Value of four shares = £1500 × 4 = £6000
   Value of two shares = £1500 × 2 = £3000
   ∴ grandchildren receive £4500, £7500, £6000, £3000

> Check your working by adding up all the shares. The total should equal the original amount.

3. A water jug fills two glasses in the ratio 5 : 3
   If the larger glass holds 250ml, how much does the small glass hold?
   What is the total capacity of the jug?

   The large glass holds 250ml and is 5 parts from the ratio.
   ∴ 1 part = 250 ÷ 5 = 50ml
   So the small glass holds 3 × 50ml = 150ml
   and the jug holds 8 parts = 8 × 50ml = 400ml

Proportion

Unit 1 ✓
Unit 2 ✓
Unit 3 ✓

> **KEY POINT**
>
> Quantities are said to be in **proportion** if their ratio stays the same as they increase or decrease. An amount may increase or decrease by a given ratio.

Convert ratio to form $n : 1$ where n is the multiplier.

Examples

1. Increase 35 in the ratio 5 : 2

$$5 : 2 = \frac{5}{2} : \frac{2}{2}$$ ← Divide both parts of the ratio by the second amount

$$= 2.5 : 1$$ ← 2.5 is the multiplier

∴ 35 increased in ratio 5 : 2 = 2.5 × 35 = 87.5

2. Decrease 24 in the ratio 4 : 5

$$4 : 5 = \frac{4}{5} : \frac{5}{5}$$ ← Divide both parts of the ratio by the second amount

$$= 0.8 : 1$$ ← 0.8 is the multiplier

∴ 24 decreased in ratio 4 : 5 = 0.8 × 24 = 19.2

Direct proportional change

Direct proportional change can be found on higher level papers.

> **KEY POINT**
>
> **Direct proportional change** is when two or more quantities increase in the same ratio.

Example

12 pens cost 90p. How much will 16 pens cost?

Find the cost of one item, then multiply by the quantity required. This is known as the **unitary method**.
One pen costs 90p ÷ 12 = 7.5p
16 pens cost 16 × 7.5p = 120p
∴ 16 pens cost £1.20 ← It is more sensible to give cost in £ and p

As the number of pens increases, so does the cost in direct proportion.

Inverse or indirect proportional change

Inverse proportional change is when one quantity increases as the other decreases in the same ratio.

Example

3 men take 5 days to paint a house. How long would 4 men take to paint the same house?

1 man would take 3 times as long as 3 men to complete the same task.
So, 1 man would take 3×5 days = 15 days
As the number of men decreases, the time taken increases in inverse proportion.

So, 4 men would take $\dfrac{15}{4}$ days

$\therefore$ 4 men would take $3\frac{3}{4}$ days.

PROGRESS CHECK

1. Simplify these ratios:
   (a) 108 : 63
   (b) 2 days : 6hrs
   (c) 24m : 60m : 1.32km
   (d) 4mins : 6mins : 90secs
2. (a) Divide 24hrs in the ratio 2 : 3 : 7
   (b) Divide £144 in the ratio 1 : 3 : 6
   (c) An orchard has white cherry trees and black cherry trees planted in the ratio 3 : 4. There are 36 black cherry trees. How many white cherry trees are there?
   (d) A triangle's sides are in the ratio 8 : 15 : 17. The perimeter is 80cm. Find the lengths of the sides of the triangle.
3. Increase these quantities in the given ratio:
   (a) 18 in the ratio 4 : 3
   (b) £39 in the ratio 7 : 3
4. Decrease these quantities in the given ratio:
   (a) 50 in the ratio 2 : 5
   (b) £72 in the ratio 4 : 5
5. Ben drives 300 miles in 5 hours of steady driving. How far can he drive in 7 hours at the same speed?
6. A fruit farmer has 14 helpers to pick his apples. They will take 12 days. How many helpers would he need to pick the apples in 8 days?

1. (a) 12 : 7 (b) 8 : 1 (c) 2 : 5 : 110 (d) 8 : 12 : 3 2. (a) 4hrs, 6hrs, 14hrs
(b) £14.40, £43.20, £86.40 (c) 27 (d) 16cm, 30cm, 34cm 3. (a) 24 (b) £91
4. (a) 20 (b) £57.60 5. 420 miles 6. 21

2.7 Approximations

After studying this section, you should be able to understand:

- rounding numbers
- estimating results
- rational numbers, irrational numbers and surds

Rounding numbers

Unit 1 ✓
Unit 2 ✓
Unit 3 ✓

> **KEY POINT**
>
> If an approximate value is required, a number may be rounded.

Rounding integers to powers of 10

A number may be rounded to the nearest 10, 100, 1000, etc.

For example, 75 378 people attend a football match at Old Trafford.

75 378 rounded to the nearest 1000 becomes 75 000 ◄ — Look at the thousands, 5378 is nearer 5000 than 6000

75 378 rounded to the nearest 100 becomes 75 400 ◄ — Look at the hundreds, 378 is nearer 400 than 300

75 378 rounded to the nearest 10 becomes 75 380 ◄ — Look at the tens, 78 is nearer 80 than 70

> **KEY POINT**
>
> It is usual to round up 'halfway' numbers. For example, if 25 is to be rounded to the nearest 10, round up to 30.

Rounding to a given number of decimal places

> **KEY POINT**
>
> Decimal places are counted to the right from the decimal point. Use d.p. as an abbreviation for decimal place. For example, 3.2 has 1 d.p. and 0.002 564 has 6 d.p.

Example

Write 36.136 to 1 decimal place and 2 decimal places.

The digit in the first decimal place is 1. The digit in the second decimal place is 3. The digit in the third decimal place is 6.

∴ 36.136 = 36.1 to 1 d.p. ◄ — 3 is less than 5 so do not round up

36.136 = 36.14 to 2 d.p. ◄ — 6 is greater than 5 so round up

Rounding to a given number of significant figures

Foundation level students will only need to round to 3 d.p. and 1 s.f.

KEY POINT

Significant figures are counted from the number's first digit from the left, disregarding zeros.

For example, 3.2 has 2 significant figures. The most significant figure is 3. 0.002 564 has 4 significant figures. The most significant figure is 2.

Use s.f. or sig. fig. as abbreviations for significant figures.

Examples

Write the following numbers to the number of significant figures given in brackets.
(a) 0.0017   (1 s.f.)

Look at the most significant figure. The next digit is 7.
As 7 is greater than 5, round up.
∴ 0.0017 = 0.002 to 1 s.f.

> The zeros in the first 2 decimal places after the decimal point keep the place value of the remaining digits. Do not put a zero in the fourth decimal place.

(b) 30 645   (3 s.f.)

Count three places from the most significant figure. The next digit is 4.
As 4 is less than 5, do not round up.
∴ 30 645 = 30 600 to 3 s.f.

> Replace the 4 and 5 with zeros to keep the place value of the remaining digits

Degree of accuracy

KEY POINT

An answer should be given to the same **degree of accuracy** as the question, unless instructed otherwise.

Example

A room measures 12.5m by 16.7m. What area of carpet is needed to cover the floor?

Area of floor = $12.5 \times 16.7 = 208.75m^2$
The original measurements were given to 1 d.p. It is sensible to give the area to the same degree of accuracy.
∴ Area of carpet = $208.8m^2$

Upper and lower bounds

Calculations involving upper and lower bounds can be found on higher level papers.

KEY POINT

When you are given an amount that has been rounded, it is useful to know the highest and lowest values it could have originally had. These are called the **upper and lower bounds**.

Example

The measurements of a piece of paper are given as 300mm by 210mm correct to the nearest 10mm. What are the highest and lowest possible values of these measurements?

300mm could be the result of rounding 295mm up to the nearest 10 or rounding $304.\dot{9}$ down to the nearest 10.
210mm could be the result of rounding 205mm up to the nearest 10 or rounding $214.\dot{9}$ down to the nearest 10.

The upper and lower bounds of the measurements are:

$295mm \leqslant 300mm < 305mm$
$205mm \leqslant 210mm < 215mm$

> It is easier to use < 305mm and < 215mm than recurring decimals as the upper bounds

See page 101 for the symbols used to represent inequalities.

Estimating results

Unit 1 ✓
Unit 2 ✓
Unit 3 ✓

Estimating a result is useful. It indicates whether your answer makes sense.

KEY POINT

To estimate a result, approximate or round each number in the calculation. This means you can work out an estimated answer quickly.

Use ≈ to mean 'approximately equal to'.

Examples

1. Estimate $519 \div 23$

   $519 \div 23 \approx 520 \div 20 = 26$ ← Round both numbers to the nearest 10
   $\therefore 519 \div 23 \approx 26$

   The actual answer, worked out by long division, or a calculator, is 22.565 correct to 3 d.p. Both answers are in the same order of magnitude (i.e. roughly the same size).

2. Estimate $\dfrac{91.4 \times 3.8}{9.9 \times 2.35}$ then compare with the actual calculation.

   $\dfrac{91.4 \times 3.8}{9.9 \times 2.35} \approx \dfrac{\overset{9}{90} \times \overset{2}{4}}{\underset{1}{10} \times \underset{1}{2}}$

   > The most sensible approximation is to 1 s.f.

   $= \dfrac{360}{20} = 18$ or by cancelling to give $\dfrac{18}{1} = 18$

   Actual answer = 14.9 to 1 d.p.
   Both answers are in the same order of magnitude.

   ≈ is used to show approximation. Then = can be used.

3. Jacob multiplies 413 by 0.025 and gets 0.103 25 as his answer. Use approximation to find if he is correct. Give a reason for your answer.

   $413 \times 0.025 \approx 400 \times 0.03 = 12$ ← Correct both amounts to 1 s.f.
   This is not of the same order of magnitude. It is much larger.
   Actual answer = 10.325
   It looks as if Jacob has his decimal point in the wrong place.

   This is a very good reason to estimate your answer first!

Rational numbers, irrational numbers and surds

Unit 1	✗
Unit 2	✓
Unit 3	✗

KEY POINT

A **rational number** is a number that can be written as a fraction with the numerator and denominator both integers.

Example of rational numbers are:

$4.75 = \dfrac{19}{4}$ $-5 = \dfrac{-5}{1}$ $2\tfrac{2}{3} = \dfrac{8}{3}$ $\sqrt{49} = \dfrac{7}{1}$ $0.625 = \dfrac{5}{8}$ $0.272\,727... = \dfrac{3}{11}$

KEY POINT

An **irrational number** cannot be written as a fraction. Decimals that neither terminate nor recur are irrational numbers.

Examples of irrational numbers are:

$\sqrt{2}$ $1 + \sqrt{5}$ $\sqrt[3]{7}$ π

KEY POINT

A **surd** is a square root that does not give an exact result, so all surds are irrational numbers.

Surds can be found on higher level papers.

For example, the following numbers are all surds:

$\dfrac{\sqrt{2}}{\sqrt{5}}$ $5 + 3\sqrt{7}$ $\sqrt[3]{7}$

The square root of a prime number is a surd and so is an irrational number.

Simplifying surds

Surds can be manipulated so that an expression is simplified. The following rules should be followed when simplifying surds ($\sqrt{a}$ and $\sqrt{b}$ are surds):

- $\sqrt{a} \times \sqrt{b} = \sqrt{ab}$
- $\dfrac{\sqrt{a}}{\sqrt{b}} = \sqrt{\dfrac{a}{b}}$
- $c\sqrt{a} + d\sqrt{a} = (c + d)\sqrt{a}$
- $c\sqrt{a} - d\sqrt{a} = (c - d)\sqrt{a}$
- $\sqrt{a} + \sqrt{b} \neq \sqrt{a + b}$ (for example, $\sqrt{5} + \sqrt{7} = 4.88$ but $\sqrt{(5 + 7)} = \sqrt{12} = 3.46$)

Examples

Simplify the following. Leave the answers in surd form.

(a) $\sqrt{45}$

$= \sqrt{9 \times 5}$ ← Write 45 as a product of its factors

$= 3\sqrt{5}$ ← The square root of 9 is 3

(b) $\dfrac{2\sqrt{72}}{3}$

$= \dfrac{2\sqrt{36 \times 2}}{3}$

$= \dfrac{2 \times 6\sqrt{2}}{3}$

$= \dfrac{12\sqrt{2}}{3}$

$= 4\sqrt{2}$ ← Cancel as 3 is a common factor

(c) $7\sqrt{12} \div \sqrt{15}$

$= \dfrac{7\sqrt{4 \times 3}}{\sqrt{5 \times 3}}$ ← Write 12 and 15 as a product of their factors

$= \dfrac{7 \times 2\sqrt{3}}{\sqrt{5} \times \sqrt{3}}$

$= \dfrac{14\sqrt{3}}{\sqrt{5}\sqrt{3}}$

$= \dfrac{14}{\sqrt{5}}$ ← Cancel as $\sqrt{3}$ is a common factor

Rationalising a denominator

KEY POINT

Rationalising a denominator means removing a surd from the denominator.

This is done by multiplying the numerator and the denominator by the surd being removed.

$\dfrac{b}{\sqrt{a}}$ ← Multiply numerator and denominator by $\sqrt{a}$

$= \dfrac{b\sqrt{a}}{a}$ ← $\sqrt{a} \times \sqrt{a} = a$

Examples

Rationalise these denominators and simplify if possible.

(a) $\dfrac{1}{\sqrt{5}}$ ← Multiply numerator and denominator by $\sqrt{5}$

$= \dfrac{\sqrt{5}}{5}$ ← Remember $\sqrt{5} \times \sqrt{5} = 5$

(b) $\dfrac{2}{\sqrt{6}}$ ← Multiply numerator and denominator by $\sqrt{6}$

$= \dfrac{2\sqrt{6}}{6}$

$= \dfrac{\sqrt{6}}{3}$ ← Cancel as 2 is a common factor

Examples

(c) $3\sqrt{\dfrac{7}{35}}$

$3\sqrt{\dfrac{\cancel{7}}{\cancel{7} \times 5}}$ ← Cancel as 7 is a common factor

$= \dfrac{3}{\sqrt{5}}$

$= \dfrac{3\sqrt{5}}{5}$ ← Multiply numerator and denominator by $\sqrt{5}$

PROGRESS CHECK

1. Round these numbers to nearest power of 10, given in brackets:
   (a) 472 (100)
   (b) 7135 (10)
   (c) 831 (10)
   (d) 13 965 (1000)
2. Correct the following to the number of d.p. or s. f. given in brackets:
   (a) 1.076 31 (1 d.p.)
   (b) 0.0625 (3 d.p.)
   (c) 946.3812 (1 s.f.)
   (d) 0.001 25 (2 s.f.)
3. Find the upper and lower bounds:
   (a) a weight of 220kg (rounded to the nearest 10kg)
   (b) an audience of 2700 (rounded to the nearest 100)
   (c) a petrol tank of 50l (rounded to the nearest 5l)
   (d) a cricket crowd of 33 000 (rounded to the nearest 1000)
4. Estimate the result without a calculator, then write down the calculator answer to a sensible degree of accuracy.
   (a) 558 × 57
   (b) 460 ÷ 77
   (c) 5972 × 233
   (d) 3792 ÷ 39
5. Simplify the following:
   (a) $\sqrt{80} - \sqrt{48}$
   (b) $3\sqrt{30} \div \sqrt{24}$
   (c) $\dfrac{1 + 3\sqrt{2}}{\sqrt{6}}$
   (d) $32\sqrt{\dfrac{6}{48}}$

1. (a) 500 (b) 7140 (c) 830 (d) 14 000 2. (a) 1.1 (b) 0.063 (c) 900 (d) 0.0013
3. (a) $215 \geqslant 220 > 225$ (b) $2650 \geqslant 2700 > 2750$ (c) $47.5 \geqslant 50 > 52.5$
(d) $32 500 \geqslant 33 000 > 33 500$ 4. (a) 33 000; 31 810 (b) 6; 5.974 (c) 1 200 000; 1 391 000
(d) 100; 97.23 5. (a) $4(\sqrt{5} - \sqrt{3})$ (b) $\dfrac{3\sqrt{5}}{2}$ (c) $\sqrt{3} + \dfrac{\sqrt{6}}{6}$ (d) $8\sqrt{2}$

2.8 Calculator use

LEARNING SUMMARY

After studying this section, you should be able to understand:

- calculator keys
- standard index form on a calculator
- exponential growth and decay

Calculator keys

Unit 1	✓
Unit 2	✗
Unit 3	✓

All calculators are different. You need to spend time getting used to your own calculator.

> **KEY POINT**
>
> Read your calculator's instruction manual carefully. It will help you to use your calculator efficiently and save you time in the exam. If the key you need is printed above a button use [SHIFT] to activate it.

Decide which Mode you wish your calculator to use.

You need to know how to use the following keys:

- **Memory**

  [M] [M−] [M+] [RCL] [STO]

  All the buttons above are examples of calculator memory keys.

  [RCL] means recall.

  [STO] means store in the memory.

- **Brackets**

  [( ] [ )]

  Brackets are used to show the order of calculating.

- **Time conversion**

  This is useful in calculations involving time which uses base 60. If your answer is displayed as a decimal this key will convert it to hours, minutes and seconds. For example:

  Your calculator displays 3.275 hours.

  [SHIFT] [=] gives 3 16 30 meaning 3hrs 16mins 30secs

  You wish to convert 1hr 38mins to a decimal and multiply by 3.

   gives the result 4.9

  (N.B. You may not need to use the [SHIFT] button on your calculator.)

- **Powers**

  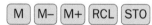

  All the buttons above are examples of calculator keys used for powers.

  x^y is used for powers other than 2 and 3.

  x^{-1} is used for reciprocals.

  10^x is used for powers of 10.

- **Roots**

  The buttons above are examples of calculator keys used for roots.

  $\sqrt[x]{}$ is used for roots other than square root and cube root.

See below for Standard index form on a calculator.

- **Exponent**

   means $\times 10^n$ where n is any power.

- **Trigonometric**

  sin cos tan

  Use the buttons above to solve trigonometric problems using angles.

  $\sin^{-1}$ $\cos^{-1}$ $\tan^{-1}$

See pages 137–142 Trigonometry.

  These are inverse trigonometric functions found using SHIFT. Use them when finding an angle.

- **Statistical**

  The buttons above are examples of calculator keys used in statistics. The SD Mode will be needed to use these keys. They are also used with y instead of x.

When you are using a calculator, it is important not to round numbers too soon, as rounding is a form of estimation. Write only the final answer to an appropriate degree of accuracy.

Standard index form on a calculator

Unit 1 ✓
Unit 2 ✗
Unit 3 ✗

KEY POINT

Use the EXP or $\times 10^x$ key to input standard index form.

Standard index form can be found on higher level papers.

Examples

1. 1.72×10^{11}

   Enter 1.72 followed by EXP 11 = or $\times 10^x$ 11 =

   The answer may be given as
   172 000 000 000 or 1.72×10^{11} or 1.72^{11} ← 11 is the power of 10. This may be shown as 1.72 11, depending on your calculator

2. $3.25 \div 10^9 = 3.25 \times 10^{-9}$

   Enter 3.25 followed by EXP (−) 9 = or $\times 10^x$ (−) 9 =

   The answer may be given as
   0.000 000 003 25 or 3.25×10^{-9} or 3.25^{-09} ← -9 is the power of 10

   If your calculator has corrected the answer to fewer decimal places, the answer may be displayed as 3^{-09} or 3×10^{-9}

Exponential growth and decay

Unit 1	✓
Unit 2	✗
Unit 3	✓

Exponential growth or decay is when a quantity grows or reduces when multiplied repeatedly by the same number, i.e. repeated percentage increase or decrease.

> Exponential growth and decay can be found on higher level papers.

KEY POINT

In order to work out a final result it is necessary to use a formula.

Repeated increase:
Final total = original amount $(1 + \text{rate of interest as a decimal})^n$

Repeated decrease:
Final total = original amount $(1 - \text{rate of interest as a decimal})^n$

(n is the number of periods of time. The number in the brackets is known as the multiplier.)

Example

A house was bought 5 years ago for £325 000. The property prices have depreciated by 4% per year. What is the value of the house today to the nearest £1000?

Value of house after 5 years = £325 000 × $(1 - 0.04)^5$

Original amount   Rate   Time

$$= £325\,000 \times 0.96^5$$
$$= £264\,996.13$$
$$= £265\,000$$

PROGRESS CHECK

Use a calculator to answer these questions

1. Work out the following. Give your answers correct to 2 d.p.
   (a) $\dfrac{2.85 \times 10^3}{7.8 \times 10^2}$
   (b) $\dfrac{5}{(3 \div 1.2)}$
   (c) $\sqrt{(3^2 + 5^2)}$
   (d) $4 + \sqrt[3]{40}$

2. A town with a population of 11 500 is growing at a rate of 2% per year. Find the population after 3 years.

3. (a) A car costs £16 000 when bought new. It loses 10% of its value in each of the first 2 years. What is its value after 2 years?
   (b) Subsequently the car's value decreases at a rate of 8% per year. What is its value when it is 5 years old?

1. (a) 3.65 (b) 2 (c) 5.83 (d) 7.42 2. 12204 3. (a) £12 960 (b) £10 091.80

Sample GCSE questions

1 Three students take a Maths test paper. The test has 25 questions. Each question has 1 mark. The pass mark is 60%.

(a) Adam says 'I only got 12 questions wrong'.

Did Adam pass the test? Explain your answer. **(1)**

(b) Jacob got $\frac{4}{5}$ of questions correct.

Did Jacob pass the test? Explain your answer. **(1)**

(c) Kizzy got exactly 64%.

How many questions did Kizzy answer correctly? **(2)**

(a) No. $\frac{12}{25} \times 100 = 48\%$. This is less than the pass mark.

Explanations always need evidence to gain marks →

(b) Yes. $\frac{4}{5} \times 100 = 80\%$. This is more than the pass mark.

(c) 64% of 25 $= \frac{64}{100} \times 25 = 16$ questions.

2 An advertisement for a summer holiday gives these details:

	7 nights	**14 nights**
1 May until 30 June	£306.50	£547.50
1 July until 25 July	£371.50	£707.50

Read these notes carefully before calculating costs →

Notes:
- prices are for one adult (16+ years)
- children (between 10 and 16 years) pay 75% of adult price
- children (less than 10 years) pay 20% of adult price
- book online for a 10% discount

(a) Miriam books a holiday for 7 nights in July. She books online for herself, her husband, Dave, and two children, Esther (12 years) and Jacob (9 years).

Explain why the total cost will be £986.34 **(4)**

(b) Mike books a holiday for 14 nights in June for two adults. The travel agent adds a percentage booking fee surcharge.

Mike's final bill is £1259.25

What was the percentage surcharge? **(3)**

(a) Cost for 2 adults $= 2 \times £371.50 = £743$

Cost for 1 child of 12 yrs $= 0.75 \times £371.50 = £278.63$

Cost for 1 child of 9 yrs $= 0.20 \times £371.50 = £74.30$

Do not forget to deduct 10% for booking online →

Total cost $= 0.90 \times £1095.93 = £986.34$

(b) Cost for 2 adults $= 2 \times £547.50 = £1095$

Surcharge $= £1259.25 - £1095 = £164.25$

Percentage surcharge $= \frac{164.25}{1095} \times 100 = 15\%$

Sample GCSE questions

Unit 1

3 a, b and c are numbers given in standard index form.

$a = 1.7 \times 10^6$ $\qquad\qquad$ $b = 2.6 \times 10^5$ $\qquad\qquad$ $c = 3.7 \times 10^4$

(a) Calculate $a + b$ **(1)**

(b) Calculate b^2 **(1)**

(c) Calculate $\dfrac{ab}{c}$ **(1)**

(a) $\begin{aligned} a + b &= 1.7 \times 10^6 + 2.6 \times 10^5 \\ &= 17 \times 10^5 + 2.6 \times 10^5 = 19.6 \times 10^5 \\ &= 1.96 \times 10^6 \end{aligned}$

(b) $\begin{aligned} b^2 &= (2.6 \times 10^5)^2 \\ &= 2.6^2 \times 10^{10} = 6.76 \times 10^{10} \end{aligned}$

(c) $\begin{aligned} \dfrac{ab}{c} &= \dfrac{1.7 \times 10^6 \times 2.6 \times 10^5}{3.7 \times 10^4} \\ &= \dfrac{1.7 \times 2.6 \times 10^{11}}{3.7 \times 10^4} = 1.19 \times 10^7 \end{aligned}$

Remember to put the answer back into standard index form

Unit 2

4 The table shows the number of students on five university campuses.

Campus	Number of students
Manchester	31 882
Leeds	30 500
Birmingham	26 300
Southampton	17 500
Bath	11 965

(a) Write the number of students on the Bath campus in words. **(1)**

(b) Write the number of students on the Manchester campus to the nearest 100. **(1)**

(c) Write the number of students on the Leeds campus to the nearest 1000. **(1)**

(d) What is the difference between the number of students at Birmingham and Southampton universities? **(1)**

(a) 11 965 = eleven thousand, nine hundred and sixty-five

(b) Number of students on the Manchester campus = 31 882 = 31 900 to the nearest 100

Remember to keep the number to the right order of magnitude

(c) Number of students on the Leeds campus = 30 500 = 31 000 to the nearest 1000

(d) Difference between number of students at Birmingham and Southampton universities = 26 300 − 17 500 = 8800

Unit 2

5 In a call centre there are 550 workers and 50 managers.

50% of the workers are employed part-time.

10% of the managers are employed part-time.

How many people in the call centre are employed part-time? **(3)**

50% of the workers = $\dfrac{1}{2} \times 550 = 275$

10% of the managers = $\dfrac{1}{10} \times 50 = 5$

Total number of people employed part-time = 280

Sample GCSE questions

Unit 2

6 A recipe gives these instructions for roasting a chicken.

> Cook for 90 minutes at 190°C.
> Increase the oven temperature to 200°C and cook for 10 minutes per kg.

Ali is going to roast a 2kg chicken.
He wants to take it out of the oven at 12.35p.m.
What is the time when the chicken should start cooking? **(4)**

Cooking time = 90 + 20 = 110mins = 1hr 50mins
1 hour before 12.35pm = 11.35am
50mins before 11.35pm = 10.45am
Chicken should start cooking at 10.45am

Work the timings out in two stages to avoid confusion

Unit 2

7 The rate of VAT is increased from 15% to 17.5%

£234 + VAT

The price of a camera is £234 plus VAT. Work out the difference in price
of the camera due to the increase in VAT. **(3)**

Difference in VAT = 17.5% − 15% = 2.5%

Difference in price = 2.5% of £234

```
=   234
  × 25
  1170
  4680
  5850   = £5.85
```

Use long multiplication as this is a non-calculator question

Remember to replace the decimal point

Unit 3

8 Megan goes shopping. She has a £20 note in her purse.
Her bus fare costs £1.40 and lunch costs £4.50
There is a special offer on at the music store.
All £16 CDs are on sale with 15% discount.
Can Megan afford to buy a CD?
Show all your working. **(4)**

There are two methods for calculating the price of a CD.

Method 1:
Discount = 15% of £16
= 0.15 × 16
= £2.40
Sale price = £16 − £2.40 = £13.60

Method 2:
Sale price = (100 − 15)% of £16
= 0.85 × 16
= £13.60

Megan spends £1.40 + £4.50 = £5.90
Change from £20 = £20 − £5.90 = £14.10
Megan has enough money to buy a CD.

Always give money to 2 decimal places

Exam practice questions

Unit 1 **1** Annie's food processor needs to be replaced. She sees one model at £110.95 including VAT.
A second model costs £97.50 excluding VAT. VAT is charged at 17.5%
   (a) Which is the better deal? Show all your working. **(2)**
   (b) When Annie returns to purchase the better deal, its price has been discounted by £20.
      What is the sale price? What percentage decrease is this? **(2)**

Unit 1 **2** Al wants to invest £15 250 for 2 years.
   There are two accounts he can use:
   ● an instant saver account, paying simple interest of 3.25% at the end of each year
   ● a 2 year account, paying 4.15% compound interest.
   Which account should Al use and why? **(5)**

Unit 1 **3** Write down **(i)** your estimate for the following and **(ii)** the accurate answer corrected to 2 d.p.
   (a) $78.41 \div 23.79$ **(1)**
   (b) 223.8×0.0047 **(1)**
   (c) $\dfrac{27.6 \times 30.51}{11.2 \times 2.71}$ **(1)**
   (d) $\dfrac{52^2}{9.8^3}$ **(1)**

Unit 1 **4** The ratio of the radius of the Earth to the radius of Saturn is approximately 1 : 10
   The ratio of the mass of the Earth to the mass of Saturn is approximately 1 : 100
   Assume that the Earth and Saturn are both spheres.
   The volume of a sphere with radius r is $\dfrac{4}{3}\pi r^3$
   (a) Show that the approximate ratio of the volume of the Earth to the volume of Saturn
      is 1 : 1000 **(1)**
   (b) Work out the approximate ratio of average density of the Earth to average density
      of Saturn in the form $1 : n$
      Use density $= \dfrac{\text{mass}}{\text{volume}}$ **(2)**
   (c) The radius of the Earth = 6 378 000m
      The radius of Saturn = 60 268 000m
      Write each radius in standard index form. **(2)**
   (d) The mass of the Earth = 5.97×10^{24}kg
      The mass of Saturn = 5.69×10^{26}kg
      What fraction is the mass of Earth to the mass of Saturn?
      Give your answer to 3 s.f. and in standard index form. **(2)**

Exam practice questions

Unit 2 **5** This table shows the temperatures on a January day in six cities in the UK. 🔢

Glasgow	-5°C
Oxford	-2°C
London	2°C
Belfast	3°C
Manchester	1°C
Cardiff	0°C

(a) Which was the warmest place? **(1)**

(b) If you were travelling between the following cities, what difference in temperature would you experience?

   (i) London to Glasgow **(1)**

   (ii) Belfast to Oxford **(1)**

   (iii) Glasgow to Manchester **(1)**

Unit 2 **6** (a) From the list of numbers below, write down: 🔢

   (i) all multiples of 5 **(1)**

   (ii) a factor of 32 **(1)**

   (iii) all square numbers **(1)**

   (iv) $\frac{2}{5}$ as a percentage. **(1)**

   55 4 80 28 49 40 35

(b) Work out $80 \div (55 - 4 - 35) \times 49$ **(2)**

Unit 2 **7** Sam buys 4 pears that cost 35p each and 3 oranges that cost 50p each. 🔢
She pays with a £5 note.
How much change should she get? **(3)**

Unit 2 **8** Aletta is 64 years old. 🔢

Her daughter, Fiona, is $\frac{5}{8}$ of her age.

Her grandson, Benjamin, is $\frac{3}{16}$ of her age.

How many years older than Benjamin is Fiona? **(3)**

Unit 2 **9** (a) Work out the value of $\sqrt{36} \times \sqrt[3]{27}$ 🔢 **(2)**

(b) Write down the value of 7^2 **(1)**

(c) Which of the following statements is true? Tick the correct box and justify your choice with an example.

   An odd number squared is always odd. ☐

   An odd number squared is always even. ☐

   The difference between squares of two odd numbers could be odd or even. ☐ **(2)**

Unit 2 **10** (a) Work out the value of $\frac{1}{3} + \frac{3}{5}$ 🔢 **(2)**

(b) Estimate the value of $\frac{\sqrt{101}}{21}$ **(2)**

Exam practice questions

Unit 2 **11** Work out the values of a, b, c and d in this magic square. The rows, columns and diagonals add up to the same number. **(4)**

10	3	14
13	d	5
a	c	b

Unit 2 **12** Naomi decides to invest money for her two children in a special savings account.
The money is invested in the same ratio as their ages 3 : 5
She invests £3200 in the older child's account.
How much is invested altogether? **(2)**

Unit 2 **13** A journal contains articles, diagrams and adverts.
$\frac{1}{5}$ of the pages are advertisements and $\frac{1}{3}$ are diagrams.

(a) What fraction of the pages are articles? **(2)**

(b) There are 36 diagrams in the journal. Some of the diagrams are graphs.
The ratio of graphs to other diagrams is 5 : 4
How many graphs are in the journal? **(2)**

Unit 2 **14** (a) Simplify $(3 + \sqrt{5})(3 + \sqrt{5})$. Give your answer in the form $a + b\sqrt{5}$ **(2)**

(b) Prove that $\frac{\sqrt{48} + 24}{\sqrt{12}} = 2(1 + 2\sqrt{3})$ **(4)**

Unit 2 **15** Put the following numbers in order of size, smallest first.

(a) 3.411   3.04   3.41   3.14 **(1)**

(b) 3   1   -3   -7   5 **(1)**

(c) $\frac{1}{3}$ $\frac{1}{4}$ $\frac{3}{8}$ $\frac{1}{2}$ **(1)**

(d) $\frac{2}{5}$ 0.3 $\frac{5}{8}$ 0.24 **(1)**

Unit 2 **16** Choose the correct symbol between each pair of numbers.

<   >   =

(a) $2\frac{5}{8}$ 2.525 **(1)**

(b) -0.78   -0.65 **(1)**

(c) $\frac{22}{7}$ 3.14 (to 2 d.p.) **(1)**

(d) 0.001963   0.0016 **(1)**

Unit 3 **17** Iqra is going to New York and exchanges £50 for dollars. £10 will buy $16.

(a) How many dollars does Iqra receive? **(2)**

(b) The following day, Iqra finds she has to cancel her trip and has to exchange the dollars back to pounds. On the following day, $30 buys £18.
How many pounds does Iqra receive? **(2)**

(c) Has Iqra lost or gained by having to exchange back from dollars to pounds? **(1)**

(d) Calculate the percentage change. **(1)**

3 Algebra

The following topics are covered in this chapter:

- Symbols
- Expressions
- Equations
- Formulae
- Inequalities
- Sequences
- Functions

3.1 Symbols

LEARNING SUMMARY

After studying this section, you should be able to understand:

- vocabulary
- using letters
- algebraic notation

Vocabulary

Unit 1 ✓
Unit 2 ✓
Unit 3 ✓

KEY POINT

The vocabulary of algebra must be learnt. It will help you to understand what a question is asking you.

- An **expression** is an algebraic statement that has letters and numbers but no equals sign.
  For example, $2x^2 + x - 3$
- An **equation** shows two equal statements or expressions.
  For example, $6 - y = 2y + 3$
- A **sequence** is a collection of terms that follow a pattern.
  For example, 1, 3, 5, 7, …
- A **term** is part of an expression, equation or sequence.
- A **formula** is an equation used to find quantities when given certain values.
  For example, $A = l \times b$
- A **function** is a relationship between variables that depend on one another.
  For example, $f(x) = x^3 - x$

> Identities can be found on higher level papers.

- An **identity** is an equation where what is on the left-hand side is the same as what is on the right-hand side for all possible values of x ($\equiv$ is used instead of =). For example, $a(b + c) \equiv ab + ac$
- A **coefficient** is a constant number or letter that multiplies an algebraic term.
  For example, $3pqr$

Using letters

Unit 1 ✓
Unit 2 ✓
Unit 3 ✓

KEY POINT

In algebra, letters are used to represent unknown numbers in expressions, formulae, equations and other algebraic functions.

Unknown **variables** in expressions and equations are usually represented by x, y and z. For example:

$x^2 + xy - 3y$ and $3z^2 + 3z + 1 = 0$

The + or – sign is attached to the term that follows it.
For example, in the expression $x^2 + xy - 3y$ above, xy is positive (+) and $3y$ is negative (–).

Unknown numbers (**constants**) are often represented by a, b and c. If these multiply a variable, they are called coefficients as in $ax^2 + by + c$.

In formulae, the unknown variables may take the initial letter of the quantities as in
$A = \pi r^2$ ⟵ A = area, r = radius
$C = \pi d$ ⟵ C = circumference, d = diameter

Algebraic notation

Unit 1 ✓
Unit 2 ✓
Unit 3 ✓

Use the following **algebraic notation** when working with letters:
- Adding letters: $c + c + c + c$ is written as $4c$
- Multiplying letters: $a \times x$ is written as ax
  $3 \times x \times y$ is written as $3xy$
  $a \times a$ is written as a^2

> Do not make the mistake of writing $a \times a$ as $2a$.

- A letter multiplied by zero always equals 0
- If the coefficient of a letter is 1, it is not necessary to write it down:
  $4y - 3y = 1y = y$

It is usual to write letters in alphabetical order and numbers are written in front of letters. For example, $q \times 4p \times 2s \times r$ is written as $8pqrs$

An expression or equation such as $3x + 2$ or $7x - 3 = 4$ is said to be linear because x has an index (power) of 1.

An expression or equation such as $2y^2 + 5y - 4$ or $y^2 - 3y + 1 = 0$ is said to be quadratic because y has an index (power) of 2.

> See page 50 for index laws.

When using powers in algebra, remember the index laws:
- $x^3 \times x^2 = x^{(3 + 2)} = x^5$
- $y^8 \div y^3 = y^{(8 - 3)} = y^5$

PROGRESS CHECK

🖩 **Without using a calculator**

1. Write as one term:
   (a) $a \times a \times a \times a$ **(b)** $\dfrac{b \times b \times b \times b}{b \times b}$ **(c)** $5 \times b \times c \times 2$ **(d)** $m \times 0$

2. **(a)** $a^5 \times a^3$ **(b)** $b^6 \div b$ **(c)** $(c^4)^3$ **(d)** $(d^6)^{\frac{1}{2}}$

1. (a) a^4 (b) b^2 (c) $10bc$ (d) 0   2. (a) a^8 (b) b^5 (c) c^{12} (d) d^3

3.2 Expressions

After studying this section, you should be able to understand:

- collecting like terms
- factorising expressions

Collecting like terms

Unit 1   ✗
Unit 2   ✓
Unit 3   ✓

KEY POINT

Like terms are those using letters with the same index. Many expressions can be simplified by **collecting like terms**.

Examples

Collect like terms:

(a) $3b + 2a - c + 5b + 3c$

     $= 2a + 3b + 5b - c + 3c$

     $= 2a + 8b + 2c$

> This expression has 1 'a' term, 2 'b' terms and 2 'c' terms

> Rearrange before simplifying

(b) $2x^2 - 3x - x^2 + 5x + y$

     $= 2x^2 - x^2 - 3x + 5x + y$

     $= x^2 + 2x + y$

> You cannot combine $x^2 + 2x$ as they have different indices

(c) $4pq + p^2 - qp + 2$

     $= p^2 + 3pq + 2$

> $q \times p = p \times q = pq$

(d) $2(x + 1) + 3x(x + 5)$

     $= 2 \times x + 2 \times 1 + 3x \times x + 3x \times 5$

     $= 2x + 2 + 3x^2 + 15x$

     $= 3x^2 + 17x + 2$

> To multiply out brackets, multiply everything inside the brackets by the term outside the bracket. Take care with negative signs.

> Write terms in order of powers.
>
> Multiply out brackets before collecting like terms.

Factorising expressions

Unit 1   ✗
Unit 2   ✓
Unit 3   ✗

KEY POINT

Factorising is the opposite of expanding or multiplying out brackets. Factorising an expression extracts a common factor.

Examples

Factorise:

(a) $2x^2 - 14x$

     $= 2(x^2 - 7x)$

     $= 2x(x - 7)$

> Common factor 2

> Common factor x

> This can be done in one step, but remember each term.

(b) $2p + 2q + 3mp + 3m^2q$

     $= p(2 + 3m) + q(2 + 3m^2)$

> Collect 2 'p' terms and 2 'q' terms

3 Algebra

Factorising quadratic expressions can be found on higher level papers.

If x has a coefficient, remember to multiply by this too.

KEY POINT

Quadratic expressions need to be factorised into two brackets.

To understand how to factorise quadratic expressions you need to know how the brackets were multiplied out.

To multiply out two brackets, the second bracket is multiplied by the first term and then by the second term.

For example:

$(x + a)(x + b)$

$= x \times x + x \times b + a \times x + a \times b$

$= x^2 + bx + ax + ab$

$= x^2 + x(a + b) + ab$

If the signs are different, but the terms are the same the expansion is called the **difference of two squares**.

For example:

$(x + a)(x - a)$

$= x \times x + x \times \text{-}a + a \times x + a \times \text{-}a$

$= x^2 - ax + ax - a^2$

$= x^2 - a^2$

Examples

Factorise:

(a) $y^2 + 5y + 6$

This is a quadratic expression and needs to be factorised into two brackets. The two brackets will look like this:

$(y \quad)(y \quad)$ ← $y \times y$ gives y^2

Now look for two factors of 6 which will give 5 when added together. Factors of 6 are 1×6 and 2×3. Only $2 + 3 = 5$

$(y + 2)(y + 3)$ ← As both signs in the expression are positive, there must be + signs in both brackets

Check your answer:
Expanding these brackets gives $y^2 + 2y + 3y + 6 = y^2 + 5y + 6$

(b) $a^2 + a - 6$ ← Coefficient of $a = 1$

The two brackets will look like this:

$(a \quad)(a \quad)$ ← $a \times a$ gives a^2

Factors of 6 are 1×6 and 2×3. Only $3 + (\text{-}2) = 1$

$(a + 3)(a - 2)$ ← As the third term in the expression is negative, there must be a + in one bracket and a – in the other bracket

Check your answer:
Expanding these brackets gives $a^2 + 3a - 2a - 6 = a^2 + a - 6$

If both the second and third terms are positive, both signs in the brackets are positive.

If the second term is negative and the third term is positive, both signs in the brackets are negative.

(c) $x^2 - 5x + 6$

The two brackets will look like this:

$(x \quad)(x \quad)$ ← $x \times x$ gives x^2

Factors of 6 are 1×6 and 2×3. Only $-3 + (-2) = -5$

$(x - 3)(x - 2)$ ← As the third term in the expression is positive, the signs in the brackets could be $+\,+$ or $-\,-$. The second term in the expression is negative, so the signs in the brackets must both be negative.

Check your answer:

Expanding these brackets gives $x^2 - 3x - 2x + 6 = x^2 - 5x + 6$

PROGRESS CHECK

 Without using a calculator

1. Collect like terms:
   (a) $2x + 3x + 2y + 3y - y$
   (b) $3(n + 5) - n + 2m$
   (c) $6(a + b) + 3(a - b)$
   (d) $3y^2 + 2xy - y - 2y^2 + x(y - 4)$

2. Factorise:
   (a) $4x^2 - x$
   (b) $y^2 - 4y - 12$
   (c) $p^2 + 10p + 21$
   (d) $z^2 - z - 20$

1. (a) $5x + 4y$ (b) $2m$ (c) $9a + 15$ (d) $y^2 + 3xy - 4x - y$ 2. (a) $x(4x - 1)$
(b) $(y + 2)(y - 6)$ (c) $(p + 3)(p + 7)$ (d) $(z - 5)(z + 4)$

3.3 Equations

LEARNING SUMMARY	After studying this section, you should be able to understand: • linear equations • simultaneous equations • quadratic equations • solving simultaneous equations of a line and a circle • trial and improvement

Linear equations

Unit 1   ✗
Unit 2   ✓
Unit 3   ✓

KEY POINT

A **linear equation** includes an unknown variable with an index of 1.
For example, $2x + 3 = 7$ is a linear equation since x has an index of 1.
When solving linear equations, it is important to keep both sides of the equation balanced at all times.

Examples

Solve the following equations:

(a) $3a = 15$

$$a = \frac{15}{3}$$ ← Divide both sides by 3 so that a is on its own

$$a = 5$$

(b) $2x + 3 = 7$

$$2x = 7 - 3$$ ← Subtract 3 from both sides of the equation, so that $2x$ is on its own

$$2x = 4$$

$$x = \frac{4}{2}$$ ← Divide both sides by 2 so that x is on its own

$$x = 2$$

(c) $\frac{c}{4} = 3$

$$c = 3 \times 4$$ ← Multiply both sides by 4 so that c is on its own

$$c = 12$$

(d) $5x - 20 = 2x - 8$

$$5x - 2x = -8 + 20$$ ← Subtract $2x$ from both sides and add 20 to both sides so that x terms and numbers are separated

$$3x = 12$$

$$x = 4$$

(e) $2(x + 5) = 5(x - 7)$ ← Multiply brackets first

$$2x + 10 = 5x - 35$$

$$35 + 10 = 5x - 2x$$

$$45 = 3x$$

$$15 = x$$ ← It does not matter that x is on the right hand side

Simultaneous equations

Unit 1 ✗
Unit 2 ✓
Unit 3 ✓

KEY POINT

Simultaneous equations are pairs of equations with two unknown variables. For example, $x + y = 18$ and $x - y = 12$. They are solved using algebra or graphs.

Simultaneous equations can be found on higher level papers.

Solving simultaneous linear equations using algebra

The **substitution** method uses one equation substituted in the other.

Example

Solve these equations for x and y.

$$4x + y = 18 \quad \boxed{1}$$ ← Labelling equations makes them easier to refer to

$$y = 2x \quad \boxed{2}$$

Substitute equation $\boxed{2}$ $(y = 2x)$ in $\boxed{1}$: ← Write down your method clearly

$$4x + 2x = 18$$

$$6x = 18$$

$$x = 3$$

From equation $\boxed{2}$ we can see that $y = 2 \times 3 \therefore y = 6$

Check your answer:

LHS (Left Hand Side) of $\boxed{1}$ = $4(3) + 6 = 12 + 6 = 18$

RHS (Right Hand Side) of $\boxed{1}$ = 18

$\therefore$ the solutions are correct.

$x = 3$ and $y = 6$

It is a good idea to check your solutions by substituting in equation $\boxed{1}$

The **elimination** method involves manipulating the equations. The first unknown is found by eliminating the second unknown. The first unknown is then substituted in one equation to find the second unknown.

Examples

Solve these simultaneous equations:

(a) $x + y = 18$ **1**

$x - y = 12$ **2**

Equation **1** + equation **2**   ← *y* terms have same coefficients so adding will eliminate *y*

$x + x + y + (-y) = 18 + 12$

$2x = 30$ ← *y* has been eliminated

$x = 15$

Substitute $x = 15$ in equation **1**:

$15 + y = 18$

$y = 18 - 15$

$y = 3$

Check your answer:

LHS of **2** $= 15 - 3 = 12$

RHS of **2** $= 12$

∴ the solutions are correct.

$x = 15$ and $y = 3$

(b) $4p + q = 17$ **1**

$p + q = 8$ **2**

Equation **1** − equation **2**   ← *q* terms have same coefficients so subtracting will eliminate *q*

$4p - p + q - (+q) = 17 - 8$

$3p = 9$ ← *q* has been eliminated

$p = 3$

Substitute $p = 3$ in equation **1**:

$4(3) + q = 17$

$12 + q = 17$

$q = 17 - 12$

$q = 5$

Check your answer:

LHS of **2** $= 3 + 5 = 8$

RHS of **2** $= 8$

∴ the solutions are correct.

$p = 3$ and $q = 5$

If your checking does not work out, your solutions are incorrect. Go back and check your working.

Remember to multiply all terms on both sides of the equation, so that it remains balanced.

KEY POINT

If neither the x nor y terms have the same coefficients, multiply first before using the elimination method.

Examples

Solve these simultaneous equations:

(a)
$$x + 3y = 7 \qquad \boxed{1}$$
$$2x + 5y = 6 \qquad \boxed{2}$$

Equation $\boxed{1} \times 2$

> Multiplying by 2 makes the coefficients of x the same

$$2x + 6y = 14 \qquad \boxed{3}$$
$$2x + 5y = 6 \qquad \boxed{2}$$

> This equation needs another label

Equation $\boxed{3}$ – equation $\boxed{2}$
$$2x - 2x + 6y - 5y = 14 - 6$$
$$y = 8$$

Substitute $y = 8$ in equation $\boxed{1}$:

> Use the original equation

$$x + 3(8) = 7$$
$$x + 24 = 7$$
$$x = 7 - 24$$
$$x = \text{-}17$$

Check your answer:

LHS of $\boxed{2}$ = 2(-17) + 5(8) = -34 + 40 = 6

RHS of $\boxed{2}$ = 6

$\therefore$ the solutions are correct.

$x = \text{-}17$ and $y = 8$

(b)
$$2x + 5y = 27 \qquad \boxed{1}$$
$$3x + 2y = 13 \qquad \boxed{2}$$

$\boxed{1} \times 3$ and $\boxed{2} \times 2$ gives $6x$ in both equations

> None of the coefficients are the same. Equal coefficients cannot be produced by a single multiplication.

or

$\boxed{1} \times 2$ and $\boxed{2} \times 5$ gives $10y$ in both equations

This example uses $\boxed{1} \times 3$ and $\boxed{2} \times 2$

$$6x + 15y = 81 \qquad \boxed{3}$$
$$6x + 4y = 26 \qquad \boxed{4}$$

> These equations need new labels

Try the other set of multiplications for yourself.

Equation $\boxed{3}$ – equation $\boxed{4}$
$$6x - 6x + 15y - 4y = 81 - 26$$
$$11y = 55$$
$$y = 5$$

Substitute $y = 5$ in equation $\boxed{1}$:
$$2x + 5(5) = 27$$
$$2x + 25 = 27$$
$$2x = 27 - 25$$
$$2x = 2$$
$$x = 1$$

Check your answer:

LHS of $\boxed{2}$ = 3(1) + 2(5) = 3 + 10 = 13

RHS of $\boxed{2}$ = 13

$\therefore$ the solutions are correct.

$x = 1$ and $y = 5$

Solving simultaneous linear equations using graphs

Examples

Solve these simultaneous equations graphically.

$y = x + 2$

$y = 8 - x$

See page 107 for how to plot straight-line graphs

Draw the lines from the two equations.

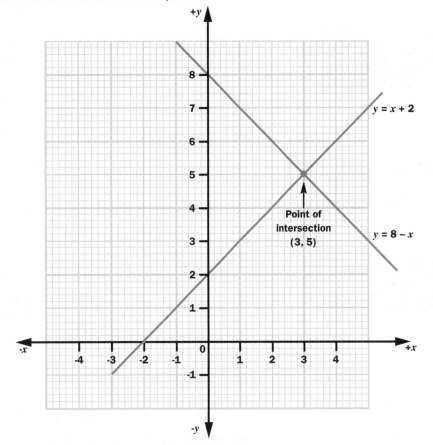

Every point on $y = x + 2$ satisfies that equation.

Every point on $y = 8 - x$ satisfies that equation.

The coordinates of the point of intersection (3, 5) satisfy both equations.

∴ the solution is $x = 3$ and $y = 5$

The coordinates of their point of intersection give the solution of the equations.

Quadratic equations

Unit 1	✗
Unit 2	✓
Unit 3	✓

Quadratic equations can be found on higher level papers.

KEY POINT

A **quadratic equation** includes the square of an unknown variable and is generally in the form $ax^2 + bx + c = 0$ although the variable may be a letter other than x.

a, b and c are constants. As there must always be an x^2 term, $a \neq 0$ but b and c can take any values: positive, negative or zero.

There are two solutions to a quadratic equation.

Solving quadratic equations by factorising

See page 88 for how to factorise expressions.

> **KEY POINT**
>
> To factorise $x^2 + bx + c = 0$ into two brackets $(x + m)(x + n)$, find two numbers m and n where $m + n = b$ and $m \times n = c$.

Examples

Solve:

If both signs in the equation are positive, there must be positive signs in both brackets.

(a) $x^2 + 7x + 12 = 0$

$(x + 3)(x + 4) = 0$

> Look for two factors of 12 which give 7 when added together. Factors of 12 are 1×12, 2×6 and 3×4. Only $3 + 4 = 7$

When the product of two numbers produces zero, one of the numbers must be zero.

Either $(x + 3) = 0$ or $(x + 4) = 0$

$\therefore \qquad x = -3$ or $x = -4$

If the b term is negative and the c term is positive, the signs in both brackets must be negative.

(b) $x^2 - 7x + 6 = 0$

$(x - 1)(x - 6) = 0$

> Factors of 6 are 1×6 and 2×3. Only $-1 + -6 = -7$

Either $(x - 1) = 0$ or $(x - 6) = 0$

$\therefore \qquad x = 1$ or $x = 6$

If the b term is positive and the c term is negative, the signs in each bracket must be different.

(c) $x^2 + x - 12 = 0$

> Coefficient of $x = 1$

$(x + 4)(x - 3) = 0$

> Factors of 12 are 1×12, 2×6 and 3×4. Only $4 + (-3) = 1$

Either $(x + 4) = 0$ or $(x - 3) = 0$

$\therefore \qquad x = -4$ or $x = 3$

(d) $y^2 - 5y - 14 = 0$

$(y - 7)(y + 2) = 0$

> Factors of 14 are 1×14 and 2×7. Only $-7 + 2 = -5$

Either $(y - 7) = 0$ or $(y + 2) = 0$

$\therefore \qquad x = 7$ or $x = -2$

(e) $2m^2 + 19m + 35 = 0$

> 1st term must be $2m \times m$ as it is $2m^2$ and both signs must be positive

$(2m + 5)(m + 7) = 0$

> Factors of 35 are 1×35 and 5×7; don't forget the $2m$

Either $(2m + 5) = 0$ or $(m + 7) = 0$

$\therefore \qquad m = -2.5$ or $m = -7$

(f) $y^2 - 3y = 0$

> In this case $c = 0$

$y(y - 3) = 0$

> Take out common factor y

Either $y = 0$ or $(y - 3) = 0$

$\therefore \qquad y = 0$ or $y = 3$

(g) $x^2 - 49 = 0$

> In this case $b = 0$

This is the difference of two squares (the signs are different but the terms are the same).

$(x - 7)(x + 7) = 0$

> $\sqrt{49} = \pm 7$

Either $(x - 7) = 0$ or $(x + 7) = 0$

$\therefore \qquad x = 7$ or $x = -7$

Solving quadratic equations by completing the square

Completing the square is a useful method for solving quadratic equations if the equation will not factorise.

Examples

Solve $x^2 + 4x = 7$ by completing the square.

$$x^2 + 4x = 7$$
$$(x + 2)^2 - 4 = 7$$
$$(x + 2)^2 = 7 + 4$$
$$(x + 2)^2 = 11$$
$$\text{so } x + 2 = \pm\sqrt{11}$$

Change the left hand side of the equation using $(x + 2)^2 = (x + 2)(x + 2) = x^2 + 4x + 4$

Add +4 to both sides of the equation

Take the square root of both sides

The solutions can be calculated or left as surds.

The two solutions are $x = -2 + \sqrt{11}$ and $x = -2 - \sqrt{11}$

If the coefficient of $x^2 \neq 1$ then divide first before completing the square.

Solving quadratic equations by formula

It is often difficult to solve a quadratic equation by factorising or completing the square particularly when $a \neq 1$. In this case use the quadratic formula.

> **KEY POINT**
>
> The solution of the quadratic equation $ax^2 + bx + c = 0$ is given by
> $$x = \frac{-b \pm \sqrt{b^2 - 4ac}}{2a}$$
> You will be given this formula but you must learn how to use it.

Examples

Solve $12x^2 + 7x = 10$ by using the quadratic formula.

$$12x^2 + 7x - 10 = 0$$
$$a = 12 \quad b = 7 \quad c = -10$$

Rearrange to general form $ax^2 + bx + c = 0$ to find the values of a, b, c

Substitute these values in the quadratic formula:

$$x = \frac{-7 \pm \sqrt{7^2 - 4(12 \times -10)}}{2 \times 12}$$
$$= \frac{-7 \pm \sqrt{49 + 480}}{24}$$
$$= \frac{-7 \pm \sqrt{529}}{24}$$

Either $x = \dfrac{-7 + \sqrt{529}}{24}$ or $x = \dfrac{-7 - \sqrt{529}}{24}$

In the formula b^2 must be greater than $4ac$ to obtain a solution

$$\therefore \quad x = 0.67 \text{ (2 d.p.) or } x = -1.25 \text{ (2 d.p.)}$$

Solving quadratic equations graphically

Using a graph is not an accurate method of solving a quadratic equation, but it is useful to know how to do it.

> **KEY POINT**
>
> Before solving graphically, a quadratic equation should be in the general form $y = ax^2 + bx + c$
> The curve is drawn and the solutions are where it crosses the x-axis ($y = 0$).

See page 111 for how to draw non-linear functions

Example

Solve $y = x^2 - x - 1$ graphically. Give solutions to 1 d.p.

x	-2	-1	0	1	2	3	0.5
y	5	1	-1	-1	1	5	-1.25

The coordinates of the minimum point will help with drawing the curve.

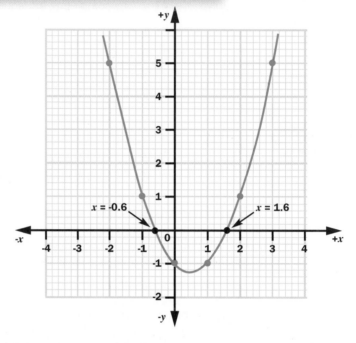

The solutions are where the graph crosses $y = 0$, which is the x-axis.

Solutions are 1.6 or -0.6 to 1 d.p.

Solving simultaneous equations of a line and a circle

Unit 1 ✗
Unit 2 ✗
Unit 3 ✓

KEY POINT

The solutions of the simultaneous equations of a line and a circle are the points of intersection of the two graphs.

The equation of a circle can be worked out using Pythagoras' theorem. The equation of any circle with centre (0, 0) and radius r is $x^2 + y^2 = r^2$.

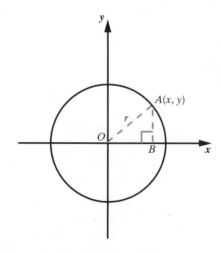

Solving simultaneous equations of a line and a circle can be found on higher level papers

See page 111 for how to draw non-linear functions

Example

Solve the equations graphically.

$x^2 + y^2 = 36$ **1**

$x + y = 1$ **2**

Equation **1** is $x^2 + y^2 = 36$ or $x^2 + y^2 = 6^2$, i.e. the equation of a circle of radius 6 units centred at the origin (0, 0).

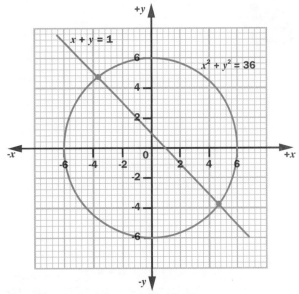

The solutions are where the graphs intersect.

∴ $x = 4.7$ and $y = -3.7$ or $x = -3.7$ and $y = 4.7$

Trial and improvement

Unit 1 ✗
Unit 2 ✗
Unit 3 ✓

KEY POINT

The **trial and improvement** method of solving equations involves testing if a value is near to the solution. Each test is more accurate until the approximate solution is reached.

Read the question carefully to find the degree of accuracy required.

It is sensible to write out your working in a logical way.

Examples

1. A solution of equation $x^3 + 2x^2 = 200$ lies between 5 and 6. Use trial and improvement to find a solution correct to 1 d.p.

   Substitute values of x in LHS of equation and compare with RHS of equation.

x	$x^3 + 2x^2$	
5	125 + 50 = 175	Too small
6	216 + 72 = 288	Too large
5.5	166.38 + 60.5 = 226.88	Too large
5.3	148.88 + 56.18 = 205.06	Just too large
5.25	144.70 + 55.13 = 199.83	Just too small

The value of x that gives exactly 200 is between 5.3 and 5.25

∴ $x = 5.3$ correct to 1 d.p.

2. A solution of equation $x^3 - 8x = 110$ lies between 5 and 6.
Use trial and improvement to find a solution correct to 1 d.p.

x	$x^3 - 8x$	
5	125 − 40 = 85	Too small
6	216 − 48 = 168	Too large
5.5	166.38 − 44 = 122.38	Too large
5.3	148.88 − 42.4 = 106.48	Just too small
5.35	153.13 − 42.8 = 110.33	Just too large

The solution is between 5 and 5.5, so a smaller increment is tried.

The value of x that gives exactly 110 is between 5.3 and 5.35

$\therefore x = 5.3$ correct to 1 d.p.

PROGRESS CHECK

1. Solve these linear equations:
   (a) $3(2x + 1) = 21$
   (b) $\frac{y}{3} + 5 = 6$
   (c) $7p - 4 = 1 - 3p$
   (d) $27 = 8 - 4m$

2. Solve these simultaneous equations algebraically:
   (a) $5a = 12 - 2b$ $4a - 3b = 5$
   (b) $3m + n = 17$ $7m - n = 23$

3. Solve these simultaneous equations graphically:
   (a) $6 - x = y$ $2x + y = 10$
   (b) $3a + b = 11$ $3a + 6b = 21$

4. Solve these quadratic equations by factorising:
   (a) $p^2 - 8p + 15 = 0$
   (b) $2n^2 + 13n + 21 = 0$

5. Solve these quadratic equations by completing the square:
   (a) $2y^2 + 18y + 40 = 0$
   (b) $x^2 + 7x + 10 = 0$

6. Solve these quadratic equations by using the quadratic formula, giving your answer to 2 d.p.
   (a) $2a^2 + 6a + 3 = 0$
   (b) $x^2 - 4x - 7 = 0$

1. (a) 3 (b) 3 (c) $\frac{2}{3}$ (d) $-4\frac{3}{4}$ 2. (a) $a = 2$ and $b = 1$ (b) $m = 4$ and $n = 5$
3. (a) $x = 4$ and $y = 2$ (b) $a = 3$ and $b = 2$ 4. (a) $p = 3$ or 5 (b) $n = -3$ or $-3\frac{1}{2}$
5. (a) $y = -4$ or -5 (b) $x = -5$ or -2 6. (a) $a = -2.37$ or -0.63 (b) $x = 5.32$ or -1.32

3.4 Formulae

LEARNING SUMMARY

After studying this section, you should be able to understand:

- deriving a formula
- substituting in a formula
- changing the subject of a formula

Deriving a formula

Unit 1   ✗
Unit 2   ✓
Unit 3   ✓

KEY POINT

A formula is an equation that shows a relationship between two or more quantities. For example:

$A = \frac{1}{2}bh$ $C = \pi d$ $v = u + at$

You may be asked to derive a formula representing a relationship.

> Think of deriving a formula as translating given information into mathematical language. If you need to use your own letter symbols, explain what they mean.

Examples

1. The length of a rectangle is $4x$ and the width is y. Write a formula representing the perimeter (P).

   Perimeter = 2 × (length + width)
   $P = 2(4x + y)$

2. Esther delivers newspapers. She is paid £10 per week, but x pence is deducted for each incorrectly delivered newspaper. In her first two weeks, five papers are delivered per week to the wrong houses. After two weeks, she is paid £18.
   (a) Write an expression for her pay for the first week.
   (b) How much does she lose for each misdelivered paper?

   (a) Let pay for 1st week be P.
   $P = 1000 - 5x$ pence ←   *Make sure all terms are in same units*
   (b) Pay for 2 weeks:
   $2(1000 - 5x) = 1800$
   $2000 - 10x = 1800$ ←   *Divide both sides by 2*
   $1000 - 5x = 900$ ←   *Subtract 900 from both sides and add $5x$ to both sides*
   $1000 - 900 = 5x$ ←
   $100 = 5x$
   $20 = x$
   Esther has 20p deducted from her wages for each misdelivered paper.

> Always give the answer in terms of the original question.

Substituting in a formula

Unit 1	✗
Unit 2	✓
Unit 3	✓

> **KEY POINT**
>
> **Substituting** given values for some variables in a formula means you can work out other values.

Examples

> Method marks are often given if the values are seen to have been substituted correctly. Do not try to jump this step.

1. The area of a triangle is given by the formula $A = \frac{1}{2}bh$.

   Find A when $b = 7$cm and $h = 6$cm.

   $A = \frac{1}{2} \times 7 \times 6$ ← A is the subject of this formula. Replace each letter with the given value

   $A = 7 \times 3$ ← Cancel by 2

   $A = 21$cm^2 ← Area is measured in cm^2

> If you are substituting negative numbers, take care with signs.

2. Temperature is converted from °F to °C by the formula $C = \frac{5(F - 32)}{9}$

   What is 75°F in °C? Give your answer to the nearest whole number.

   $C = \frac{5(75 - 32)}{9}$

   $C = \frac{5 \times 43}{9}$

   $C = 23.\dot{8}$

   $C = 24$°C to nearest degree

Changing the subject of a formula

Unit 1	✗
Unit 2	✓
Unit 3	✗

You may need to rearrange a formula to make a calculation easier.

> **KEY POINT**
>
> When **changing the subject of a formula**, follow the same rules for manipulating an equation.

Example

Find 18°C in °F using the temperature formula $C = \frac{5(F - 32)}{9}$

You can substitute 18°C into the formula and then calculate °F or you can change the subject of the formula to F.

$C = \frac{5(F - 32)}{9}$

$9C = 5(F - 32)$ ← Multiply both sides by 9

$\frac{9C}{5} = F - 32$ ← Divide both sides by 5

$\frac{9C}{5} + 32 = F$ ← Add 32 to both sides

> This can be written $F = \frac{9C}{5} + 32$

Now substitute C = 18° into the rearranged formula.

$F = \frac{9 \times 18}{5} + 32 = 32.4 + 32$

$\therefore F = 64.4$°F

1 **(a)** A cooking guide for roasting beef is given as 25mins per given weight (w) plus an extra 20mins. Write a formula to find how long (T) it would take to roast a joint of beef.

(b) The cost (C) of hiring a car, with mileage included, is £126 per week (w) plus £3.30 insurance per day (d). Write a formula to find C.

2 Calculate by substituting the given values in these formulae. Give answers to 3 s.f. where necessary.

(a) $V = lbh$ (V when $l = 3.5$, $b = 2$, $h = 4.2$)

(b) $v = u + at$ (t when $u = 5$, $a = 4$, $v = 6$)

(c) $A = \pi r^2$ (r when $A = 32$)

(d) $v^2 = u^2 + 2as$ (v when $u = 3$, $a = 4.2$, $s = 5$)

3 Make the letter given in brackets the subject of these formulae:

(a) $I = \dfrac{PRT}{100}$ (R)

(b) $V = \pi r^2 h$ (r)

(c) $r^2 = \dfrac{4\pi}{A}$ (A)

(d) $P = 2(l + w)$ (w)

1. (a) $T = 25w + 20$ (b) $C = 126w + 3.30d$ 2. (a) 29.4 (b) 0.25 (c) 3.19 to 3 s.f. (d) 7.14 to 3 s.f.
3. (a) $R = \dfrac{100I}{PT}$ (b) $r = \sqrt{\dfrac{V}{\pi h}}$ (c) $A = \dfrac{4\pi}{r^2}$ (d) $w = \dfrac{P}{2} - l$

3.5 Inequalities

After studying this section, you should be able to understand:

- representing inequalities
- solving an inequality

Representing inequalities

Unit 1	✗
Unit 2	✓
Unit 3	✗

These symbols are used to **represent inequalities**:

- $x < 4$ (x is less than 4)
- $x > 7$ (x is greater than 7)
- $y \leqslant 10$ (y is less than or equal to 10)
- $y \geqslant -3$ (y is greater than or equal to -3)

Number lines are also used to illustrate inequalities:

- An included number is shown by a filled circle.
- A number not included is shown by an empty circle.

Examples

Show the following on number lines.

(a) $x \geqslant -2$

(b) $-1 \leqslant x < 3$

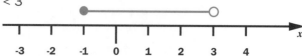

(c) $5 \geqslant 2y - 1 > 1$

This must be arranged so that y is on its own. The inequality is a combination of:

$5 \geqslant 2y - 1$ and $2y - 1 > 1$

$6 \geqslant 2y$ $2y > 2$ ← Add 1 to both sides in both inequalities

$3 \geqslant y$ $y > 1$ ← Divide both sides by 2

so $3 \geqslant y > 1$

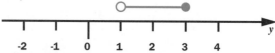

Solving an inequality

Unit 1   ✗
Unit 2   ✓
Unit 3   ✗

KEY POINT

When **solving an inequality**, follow the same procedure used for solving an equation, except when multiplying or dividing each side by a negative number you must reverse the inequality.

Solving an inequality with one variable

Examples

Solve these inequalities:

(a) $5 - 3x \leqslant 1$

        $5 \leqslant 1 + 3x$ ← Add $3x$ to both sides

    $5 - 1 \leqslant 3x$ ← Subtract 1 from both sides

       $4 \leqslant 3x$

       $\dfrac{4}{3} \leqslant x$ ← Divide both sides by 3

or $x \geqslant 1\frac{1}{3}$

(b) $8 - 2x > 10$

It is sensible to divide the whole inequality by 2, so that the coefficient of $x = 1$.

$4 - x > 5$

    $-x > 5 - 4$ ← Subtract 4 from both sides

    $-x > 1$

Now divide the whole inequality by -1, so that you will have x on LHS instead of $-x$.

Remember that dividing by a negative number reverses the inequality.

$\therefore x < -1$

Solving an inequality with two variables

Inequalities with two variables can be found on higher level papers.

KEY POINT

If an inequality has two variables such as $x + y > 4$ you need to draw the straight line of the corresponding equation. Look at the areas above and below the line. These are called regions and are the solutions of the inequality.

For the equation of a straight-line graph, see page 107.

Example

Solve $x + y > 4$ and shade the region that satisfies this inequality.

Rearrange the equation into the form $y = mx + c$. This gives $y = -x + 4$.
Work out the coordinates for $y = -x + 4$ and draw a straight-line graph.

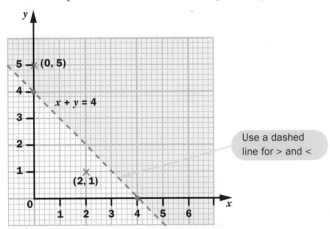

Use a dashed line for > and <

The line $y = 4 - x$ intercepts both axes at 4. Try substituting $x = 0$, then $y = 0$ to see why.

Choose two points, one below the line and one above, then substitute coordinates into LHS of inequality.
(2, 1) below the line gives $2 + 1 = 3 \rightarrow x + y < 4$
(0, 5) above the line gives $0 + 5 = 5 \rightarrow x + y > 4$
All the points below the line give $x + y < 4$
so the shaded area above the line gives $x + y > 4$

Graphs showing more than one inequality

Example

Shade the region that is satisfied by $x \geqslant 0$, $y \leqslant 2$ and $4y + 3x < 12$

The equation of the x-axis is $y = 0$.

The equation of the y-axis is $x = 0$.

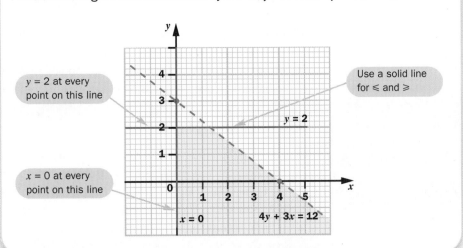

$y = 2$ at every point on this line

Use a solid line for $\leqslant$ and $\geqslant$

$x = 0$ at every point on this line

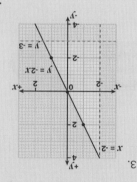
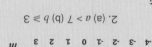
3.6 Sequences

LEARNING SUMMARY

After studying this section, you should be able to understand:

- generating sequences
- nth term

Generating sequences

Unit 1	✗
Unit 2	✓
Unit 3	✗

KEY POINT

A **sequence** is a collection of **terms** that follow a pattern or rule.

Sequences can be generated in several ways. You may be given the first few terms of a sequence and asked to generate the next few terms.

- Some sequences are generated by adding or subtracting the same number each time, called a **common difference**. For example:

  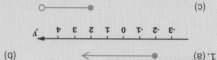

  1, 4, 7, 10, ...   Each term is found by adding 3 to the previous term
  +3 +3 +3

- Some sequences are generated by multiplying or dividing by the same number, called a **constant**. For example:

  2, 4, 6, 8, ...   The position of the term is multiplied by 2
  1×2 2×2 3×2 4×2

- Some sequences are square numbers or cube numbers. For example:

  1, 4, 9, 16, ...   The position of the term is squared
  1^2 2^2 3^2 4^2

> There are many other possible patterns. You may have to multiply a term and then add a number to get the next term. It is important to find the pattern or rule governing the sequence.

nth term

Unit 1   ✗
Unit 2   ✓
Unit 3   ✗

KEY POINT

The **nth term** is a general formula for a sequence where n is the position of the term, i.e. the first term has $n = 1$.

Example

Find the nth term of these sequences.

(a) 2, 4, 6, 8, ...

1st term $= 1 \times 2 = 2$ ← It is a good idea to number the terms
2nd term $= 2 \times 2 = 4$
3rd term $= 3 \times 2 = 6$
4th term $= 4 \times 2 = 8$

> Watch out for squares and cubes of numbers as well as triangular numbers.

Position of term   Constant   Term

nth term $= n \times 2$
$\qquad\quad = 2n$

b) (i) 5, 8, 11, 14, ...

1st term $= 1 \times 3 + 2 = 5$ ← The constant is 3, but the first term is 5 so you also need to add 2
2nd term $= 2 \times 3 + 2 = 8$
3rd term $= 3 \times 3 + 2 = 11$
4th term $= 4 \times 3 + 2 = 14$

Position of term $\times$ constant $+ 2$ Term

nth term $= n \times 3 + 2$
$\qquad\quad = 3n + 2$

ii) If the sequence had been written 2, 5, 8, 11, ...

1st term $= 0 \times 3 + 2 = 2$ ← The constant 3 is multiplied by 1 less than the position of the term
2nd term $= 1 \times 3 + 2 = 5$
3rd term $= 2 \times 3 + 2 = 8$
4th term $= 3 \times 3 + 2 = 11$

nth term $= 3(n - 1) + 2$
$\qquad\quad = 3n - 3 + 2$
$\qquad\quad = 3n - 1$

You may be asked to find specific terms of a sequence by substituting in the nth term.

Example

Find the 8th term of a sequence with nth term $= 2n - 3$.

8th term $= 2(8) - 3$
$\qquad\quad = 16 - 3$
$\qquad\quad = 13$

3.7 Functions

LEARNING SUMMARY

After studying this section, you should be able to understand:

- coordinates
- linear functions
- graphs for real-life situations
- non-linear functions
- transformation of functions

Coordinates

Unit 1	✗
Unit 2	✓
Unit 3	✓

KEY POINT

Coordinates are pairs of numbers that give the position of a point on a graph or grid. They are given in the form (x, y) and plotted using a dot or small cross.

A sharp pencil is necessary to plot and join the points as accurately as possible.

Label the axes as shown. Make sure there is a comma between coordinates and give the x coordinate first.

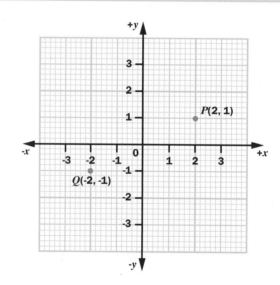

Linear functions

Unit 1	✗
Unit 2	✓
Unit 3	✓

A linear function is given in the form:

$y = mx + c$ ← | c is the intercept on the y-axis |

| m is the gradient |

$y = mx + c$ is the general equation of a straight line and is the rule for all points on the line. To draw a straight-line graph a selection of coordinates is plotted. It is useful to have a table of coordinates. When you are given values of x, the values of y can be calculated. You may be given a range of values or have to choose your own.

> Foundation level students will need to be able to recognise and draw linear functions.

Example

Draw the graph of $y = 2x + 1$ for $-2 \leqslant x \leqslant 1$.

x	-2	-1	0	1
y	-3	-1	1	3

← | Substitute values of x in $2x + 1$ to find values of y |

> Remember signs when calculating.

> A straight-line graph can be drawn using two points, but it is more accurate to use at least three points.

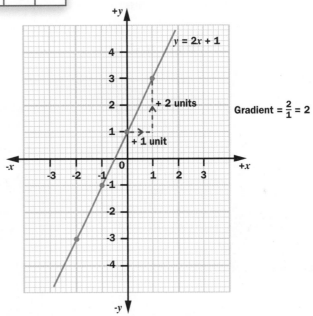

Gradient $= \frac{2}{1} = 2$

The line cuts the y-axis at $y = 1$. This is called the **intercept**.
The slope of the line is the **gradient**. This is calculated by:

$$\frac{\text{Vertical change}}{\text{Horizontal change}}$$

If the line goes 'uphill', as in this example, the gradient is positive. If the line goes 'downhill' the gradient is negative. As the gradient increases, the line gets steeper.

> If the intercept is 0, the line passes through the origin (0, 0).

Finding the equation of a straight-line graph

The equation of a straight-line graph can be found if you are given the gradient and the y-intercept.

Examples

1. What are the equations of these straight lines?

    (a) Gradient = 1, passing through point (0, -5)

    $y = mx + c$ ← General equation

    $y = (1)x + (-5)$

    $y = x - 5$

    (b) Gradient = $-\dfrac{3}{4}$, passing through point (0, 2)

    $y = mx + c$

    $y = (-\dfrac{3}{4})x + (2)$

    $y = -\dfrac{3}{4}x + 2$

    This could be written as $4y = 8 - 3x$ ← Multiply both sides by 4

2. Find the gradient and y-intercept of this straight line.

    $y = 4x + 1$ ← Compare with $y = mx + c$

    gradient = 4 as $m = 4$

    y-intercept = 1 as $c = 1$

Parallel lines

KEY POINT

If lines are parallel, they have the same gradient.

The gradient of parallel and perpendicular lines can be found on higher level papers.

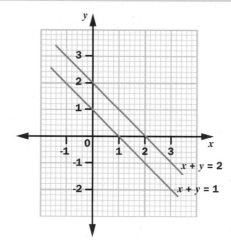

$x + y = 2$

$x + y = 1$ ← Gradient of both lines = -1

Example

What is the equation of a line passing through (0, -2) and parallel to $y = 3x + 2$?

Gradient must be 3 as $m = 3$ and lines are parallel.

y-intercept = -2

∴ equation is $y = 3x - 2$

If the gradients (m) are equal, lines are parallel.

Perpendicular lines

KEY POINT

If lines are perpendicular to each other, i.e. at 90° to one another, the product of their gradients = -1.

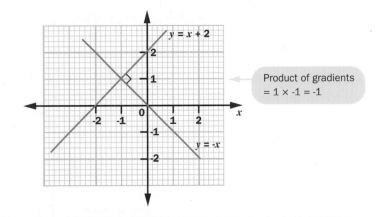

Product of gradients
= 1 × -1 = -1

Example

What is the gradient of a line perpendicular to $y = 3x + 1$?

If gradient of first line is m_1, then $m_1 = 3$.
If gradient of perpendicular line is m_2
$m_1 \times m_2 = -1$
$3 \times m_2 = -1$
$3m_2 = -1$
$m_2 = -\frac{1}{3}$ ← Gradient of perpendicular line

If the product of gradients ($m_1 m_2$) = -1, lines are perpendicular to each other.

Graphs for real-life situations

Unit 1 ✗
Unit 2 ✓
Unit 3 ✓

Information for real-life situations can be represented on graphs. One quantity is plotted against another quantity, such as distance and time.

● **Distance–time graph**
Joseph's journey is shown on this graph.

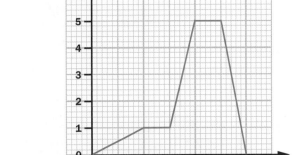

Time is always on the horizontal axis. Read values for time and distance off the graph.

The gradient of each sloping line is Joseph's speed at that particular time.
0700 – 0800: speed = 1km ÷ 1hr
= 1km/hr
0800 – 0830: the line is horizontal (gradient = 0)
This means Joseph is stationary.
0830 – 0900: speed = 4km ÷ 0.5hr
= 8km/hr
0900 – 0930: Joseph is stationary.
0930 – 1000: Joseph returns home at speed = 5km ÷ 0.5hr = 10km/hr

The slope is steeper between 0930 and 1000 indicating a faster speed.

- **Speed–time graphs**

  The gradient of a speed–time graph shows acceleration. The steeper the slope, the greater the acceleration. A horizontal line means a steady speed with no acceleration.

  It may look like this:

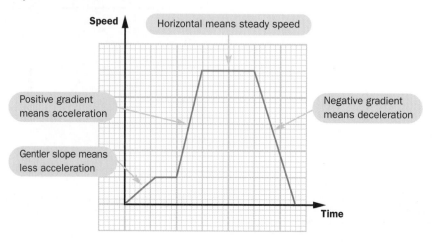

- **Matching graphs to situations**

  Three containers are filled with water. These graphs illustrate how the depth of water changes with time.

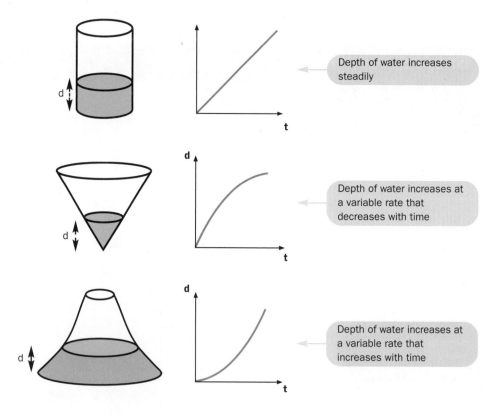

Non-linear functions

Unit 1	✗
Unit 2	✓
Unit 3	✓

To draw a graph of any non-linear function, calculate a table of coordinates and plot these points. The result will be a curve, not a straight line, so do not use a ruler to join points. Draw a smooth curve through all the points, continuing past the final points plotted. If a point seems out of line, check your calculation.

Quadratic function

> Foundation level students will need to be able to recognise and draw quadratic functions.

KEY POINT

A **quadratic function** will include the square of a variable. The curve will always be U-shaped and is also called a parabola.

Examples

1. Draw the graph of $y = x^2 + 2$

x	-2	-1	0	1	2
y	6	3	2	3	6

> $+x$ and $-x$ give the same values of y as x^2 is used

> Use a sharp pencil to draw the graph. Do not use a pen as you may make a mistake.

> Marks are awarded for drawing a smooth curve.

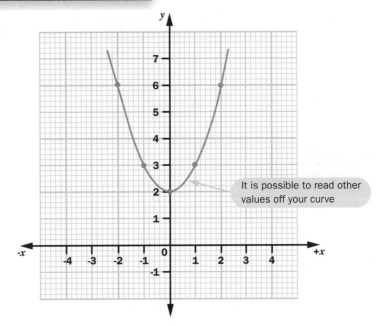

> It is possible to read other values off your curve

2. Solve these simultaneous equations for x.

$y = x^2 + 3$

$y = 4 - x$

> The point of intersection will give the solutions as the coordinates will satisfy both equations

Draw the graphs for $-2 \leqslant x \leqslant 2$

$y = x^2 + 3$

x	-2	-1	0	1	2
y	7	4	3	4	7

$y = 4 - x$

x	-2	-1	0	1	2
y	6	5	4	3	2

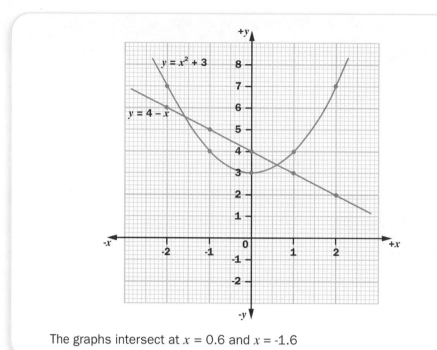

You do not need to give the *y* coordinate in this example as you are solving the equations for *x*.

The graphs intersect at $x = 0.6$ and $x = -1.6$

Cubic function

KEY POINT

A **cubic function** will include the cube of a variable. It will always be S-shaped.

Other non-linear functions can be found on higher level papers

Example

Draw the graph of $y = x^3 + x - 5$

x	-2	-1	0	1	2
y	-15	-7	-5	-3	5

When you substitute negative values in x^3, the result is negative

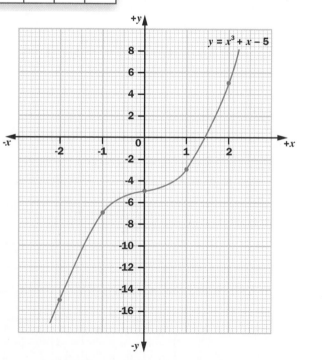

Reciprocal function

> **KEY POINT**
>
> A **reciprocal function** always has x in the denominator of the fraction:
>
> $f(x) = \dfrac{1}{x}$ $y = \dfrac{2}{x}$ $f(x) = \dfrac{1}{3+x}$

You cannot divide by zero so there is no point at $x = 0$

Example

Draw the graph of $y = \dfrac{3}{x}$ for $-4 \leqslant x \leqslant 4$.

x	-4	-3	-2	-1	1	2	3	4
y	$-\frac{3}{4}$	-1	$-1\frac{1}{2}$	-3	3	$1\frac{1}{2}$	1	$\frac{3}{4}$

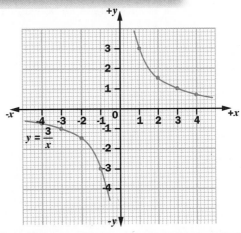

$y = \dfrac{3}{x}$

Exponential function

> **KEY POINT**
>
> The **exponential function** is in the form $f(x) = k^x$ where k is a constant:
>
> $y = 2^x$ $f(x) = 3^x$
>
> The index or exponent is the variable x.

See page 49 for Index notation.

Example

Draw the graph of $y = 2^x$ for $-4 \leqslant x < 3$.
Give values of y to 2 d.p.

When $x = 0$, $y = 1$ whatever the value of k. y is always positive.

x	-4	-3	-2	-1	0	1	2
y	0.06	0.13	0.25	0.5	1	2	4

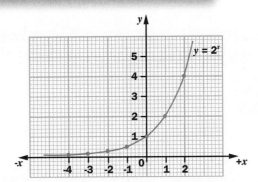

$y = 2^x$

See pages 137–142 Trigonometry.

Trigonometrical functions

> **KEY POINT**
>
> You need to be able to recognise the graphs of the following
> **trigonometric functions**:
>
> $f(x) = \sin x°$ $f(x) = \cos x°$ $f(x) = \tan x°$
>
> These are also called **circular functions**.
>
> They are periodic functions as their values repeat. The sine and cosine
> functions have a period of 360° and the tangent function has a period of 180°.

The graphs $y = \sin x°$, $y = \cos x°$ and $y = \tan x°$ are plotted for $0 \leqslant x \leqslant 360°$
y values are found using a calculator.

- **Sine function:** $y = \sin x°$

  The sine curves lie between 1 and -1.

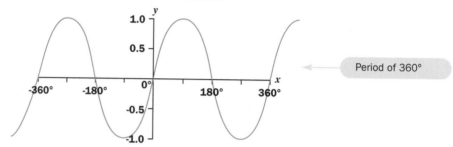

Period of 360°

- **Cosine function:** $y = \cos x°$

  The cosine curves lie between 1 and -1.

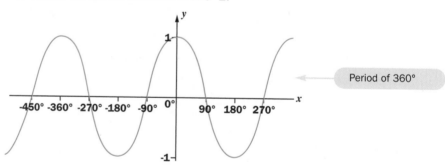

Period of 360°

- **Tangent function:** $y = \tan x°$

  There is no limit on the tangent curves.

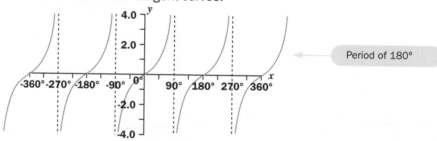

Period of 180°

Transformation of functions

Unit 1	✗
Unit 2	✗
Unit 3	✓

The graph of a function can be transformed by...
- translating
- stretching
- compressing
- reflecting.

Both the position and size of the graph may be affected.

Transformations of functions can be found on higher level papers.

Translation of functions

If y = 'an expression involving x' then it can be written as $y = f(x)$.

If $f(x)$ is the function and $a > 0$
- $y = f(x) + a$ moves the original graph 'a' units up ($\uparrow$) the y-axis
- $y = f(x) - a$ moves the original graph 'a' units down ($\downarrow$) the y-axis
- $y = f(x - a)$ moves the original graph 'a' units to the right ($\rightarrow$)
- $y = f(x + a)$ moves the original graph 'a' units to the left ($\leftarrow$)

This moves the graph in the opposite direction to what you would expect.

For example:

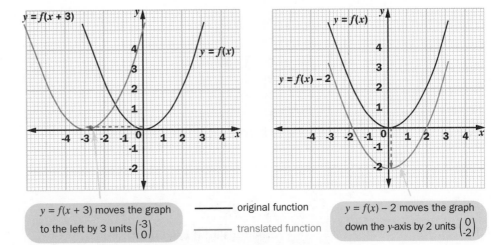

$y = f(x + 3)$ moves the graph to the left by 3 units $\binom{-3}{0}$

—— original function
—— translated function

$y = f(x) - 2$ moves the graph down the y-axis by 2 units $\binom{0}{-2}$

Stretching and compressing functions

If $f(x)$ is the function
- $y = af(x)$ stretches the original graph along the y-axis by a factor of a. If $a > 1$, e.g. $y = 2x^2$, the y-coordinates of all the points are multiplied by a factor of 2. If $a < 1$, e.g. $y = 0.5x^2$, the y-coordinates are multiplied by a factor of 0.5
- $y = f(ax)$ stretches the original graph along the x-axis by a factor of a. If $a > 1$, all the points are stretched inwards in the x direction by a factor of $\frac{1}{a}$, e.g. if $y = (2x)^2$, the x-coordinates are multiplied by $\frac{1}{a} = \frac{1}{2} = 0.5$. If $a < 1$, all the points are stretched outwards in the x direction by a factor of $\frac{1}{a}$, e.g. if $y = (0.5x)^2$, the x-coordinates are multiplied by $\frac{1}{a} = \frac{1}{0.5} = 2$

For example:

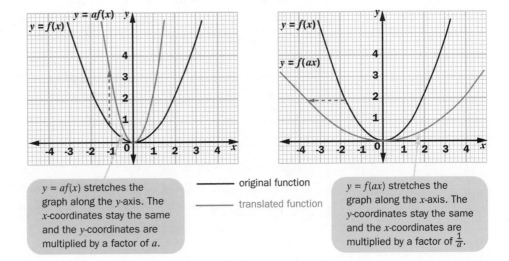

$y = af(x)$ stretches the graph along the y-axis. The x-coordinates stay the same and the y-coordinates are multiplied by a factor of a.

—— original function
—— translated function

$y = f(ax)$ stretches the graph along the x-axis. The y-coordinates stay the same and the x-coordinates are multiplied by a factor of $\frac{1}{a}$.

Reflection of functions

See page 149
Transformations.

KEY POINT

Reflection of function $y = f(x)$ in the x-axis gives $y = -f(x)$.
Reflection of function $y = f(x)$ in the y-axis gives $y = f(-x)$.

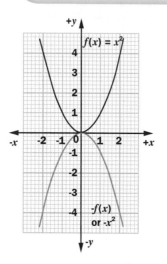

—— original function

—— reflected function

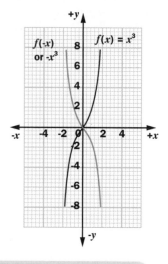

PROGRESS CHECK

Without using a calculator

1. Find the gradients and intercepts of these lines:
   (a) $y = 2x - 4$ **(b)** $3y = x + 6$ **(c)** $2y = 3 - 8x$

2. Write down the equations of these straight lines:
   (a) Line parallel to $2y + 4x = 1$, y-intercept = -3
   (b) Line perpendicular to $y = 2x + 5$, y-intercept = 7

3. The graph opposite illustrates a motorcyclist's journey.
   (a) Which sections show when the motorcyclist was stationary?
   (b) Which section shows when the motorcyclist was at his fastest?
   (c) Which section shows when the motorcyclist was at his slowest?

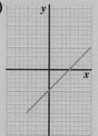

4. Which of the following equations goes with each curve?
   $y = x^3 - 3x$ $y = 3x^2 + 2$ $y = x - 3$
   (a)   **(b)**   **(c)**

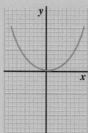

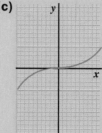

4. (a) $y = 3x^2 + 2$ (b) $y = x - 3$ (c) $y = x^3 - 3x$
2. (a) $y = -2x - 3$ (b) $y = 7 - \frac{x}{2}$ or $2y + x = 14$ 3. (a) B and D (b) E (c) A
1. (a) gradient = 2, y-intercept = -4 (b) gradient = $\frac{1}{3}$, y-intercept = 2 (c) gradient = -4, y-intercept = $1\frac{1}{2}$

Sample GCSE questions

Unit 2

1 (a) Simplify $a^2 \times a^3$ **(1)**

(b) Simplify $\dfrac{a^5}{a^2}$ **(1)**

(c) Simplify $\sqrt{\dfrac{9\pi r^3}{\pi r}}$ **(2)**

Learn the index laws

(a) $a^2 \times a^3 = a^{2+3} = a^5$

(b) $\dfrac{a^5}{a^2} = a^{5-2} = a^3$

(c) $\sqrt{\dfrac{9\pi r^3}{\pi r}} = \sqrt{9r^2} = 3r$

Unit 2

2 (a) The first three terms of a sequence are 2, 4, 10.
Find the next term by following the rule:
'Multiply the previous term by 3 and subtract 2'. **(1)**

(b) A different sequence generates terms by multiplying the previous
term by 3 and subtracting p where p is an integer. The first term
is 6 and the fourth term is 136.
Work out the value of p. **(4)**

(a) Next term $= (10 \times 3) - 2 = 28$

(b) 2nd term $= (3 \times 6) - p = 18 - p$

3rd term $= 3(18 - p) - p = 54 - 4p$

4th term $= 3(54 - 4p) - p = 162 - 13p = 136$

$162 - 136 = 13p$

$26 = 13p$

$\therefore p = 2$

Unit 2

3 (a) Factorise $18a^3 + 12abc$ **(2)**

(b) Factorise $a^2 + 5a + 6$ **(2)**

(c) Simplify $b + \dfrac{1}{5}(b + 1)$ **(1)**

(d) Factorise $5a^2 - 45b^2$ **(3)**

Don't forget to look at number factors as well as letters

(a) $18a^3 + 12abc = 6a(3a^2 + 2bc)$

(b) $a^2 + 5a + 6 = (a + 2)(a + 3)$

(c) $b + \dfrac{1}{5}(b + 1) = \dfrac{6b + 1}{5}$

(d) $5a^2 - 45b^2 = 5(a + 3b)(a - 3b)$ or $5(a^2 - 9b^2)$

Unit 2

4 Two families go to the cinema.
The Wycombe family pay £14 for one adult and three children.
The Marlow family pay £22 for two adults and four children.
Work out the cost of an adult ticket and a child ticket. **(5)**

Always explain the letters you are using

Let an adult's ticket cost £A and let a child's ticket cost £C.

$A + 3C = 14$　**1**

$2A + 4C = 22$　**2**

Multiply equation **1** by 2: $2A + 6C = 28$　**3**

It helps to label your equations

Equation **3** – equation **2** : $2C = 6 \therefore C = 3$

Substitute $C = 3$ in equation **1** : $A + 9 = 14$

$A = 5$

An adult's ticket costs £5 and a child's ticket costs £3.

Sample GCSE questions

Unit 2

5 **(a)** Solve the inequality $m + 6 < 4m + 9$ **(2)**

(b) Make m the subject of the formula $2n = \sqrt{4 + 3m}$ **(2)**

(a) $m + 6 < 4m + 9$

$6 - 9 < 4m - m$

$-3 < 3m$

$\therefore -1 < m$

Be careful with negative signs

(b) $2n = \sqrt{4 + 3m}$

$4n^2 = 4 + 3m$

$4n^2 - 4 = 3m$

$\dfrac{(4n^2 - 4)}{3} = m$

$\therefore m = \dfrac{4(n^2 - 1)}{3}$

Unit 3

6 Solve $\dfrac{2}{x + 2} + \dfrac{3}{x + 1} = 5$ giving your answer to 3 s.f. **(6)**

$2(x + 1) + 3(x + 2) = 5(x + 2)(x + 1)$

$2x + 2 + 3x + 6 = 5x^2 + 15x + 10$

$5x + 8 = 5x^2 + 15x + 10$

giving $5x^2 + 10x + 2 = 0$

Use the quadratic formula:

$x = \dfrac{-b \pm \sqrt{b^2 - 4ac}}{2a}$

$x = \dfrac{-10 \pm \sqrt{10^2 - (4 \times 5 \times 2)}}{(2 \times 5)}$

$x = \dfrac{-10 \pm \sqrt{100 - 40}}{10}$

$x = \dfrac{-10 \pm \sqrt{60}}{10}$

solutions: either $x = \dfrac{-10 + \sqrt{60}}{10}$ or $x = \dfrac{-10 - \sqrt{60}}{10}$

Remember to work out both solutions

either $x = -0.225$ or $x = -1.77$

Unit 3

7 **(a)** If $a = 3$, $b = -1$, $c = 2$, find the value of:

(i) $3a + 2b + c$ **(1)**

(ii) $\dfrac{ac - bc}{2c}$ **(2)**

(b) Simplify $5m + 4n - 3m + n$ **(2)**

(c) Solve $3p - 4 = 2 - 9p$ **(3)**

(a) (i) $3a + 2b + c = 3(3) + 2(-1) + 2 = 9 - 2 + 2 = 9$

(ii) $\dfrac{ac - bc}{2c} = \dfrac{(3 \times 2) - (-1 \times 2)}{2 \times 2} = \dfrac{6 + 2}{4} = \dfrac{8}{4} = 2$

(b) $5m + 4n - 3m + n = 2m + 5n$

(c) $3p - 4 = 2 - 9p$

$3p + 9p = 2 + 4$

$12p = 6$

$p = \dfrac{6}{12} = \dfrac{1}{2}$

Sample GCSE questions

Unit 3

8 The end of year Prom at a school has 152 students seated at 14 tables.
There are 10 or 12 students at each table.
How many tables have 12 people? **(4)**

Always define your letters

Let the number of tables with 10 = t; let number of tables with 12 = s

$t + s = 14$ so $t = 14 - s$ **①**

$10t + 12s = 152$ **②**

Substitute equation **①** in equation **②**

$10(14 - s) + 12s = 152$

$140 - 10s + 12s = 152$

$140 + 2s = 152$

$2s = 152 - 140$

$2s = 12$

$s = 6$

There are 6 tables with 12 people.

Unit 3

9 Judy uses the quadratic formula to solve a quadratic equation.
She substitutes values into the formula:

$$x = \frac{5 \pm \sqrt{25 - 84}}{6}$$

(a) What quadratic equation is Judy trying to solve? **(2)**

(b) Will Judy be able to solve the equation? Explain your answer. **(1)**

(a) General equation is $ax^2 + bx + c = 0$

The quadratic formula is $x = \dfrac{-b \pm \sqrt{b^2 - 4ac}}{2a}$

From Judy's substitution:

$a = \dfrac{6}{2} = 3$

$b = -5$

$c = \dfrac{84}{(4 \times 3)} = 7$

The quadratic equation Judy is trying to solve is $3x^2 - 5x + 7 = 0$

(b) Judy cannot solve the equation.

It is important to remember this reason

In the formula b^2 must be greater than $4ac$ to obtain a solution and in this case $b^2 < 4ac$.

Exam practice questions

Unit 2 **1** Simplify: 🔢
   (a) $4c + 2d + 2d + 5c - de$ (1)
   (b) $5m + 2n - n + mn$ (1)
   (c) $xy + 2yz - 2zy + 6yx$ (1)
   (d) $6pq \times (-3p^2q)$ (2)
   (e) $3(a + b) - 3(5a + 4b)$ (2)

Unit 2 **2** $a = 2, b = -1, c = 3$ 🔢
   Find the value of:
   (a) $2a + b + 2c$ (1)
   (b) $a - 3b + 4c$ (1)
   (c) $(a + b)(a - c)$ (1)
   (d) $a^2 + b^3 + c^2$ (2)
   (e) $b^2 + \sqrt{(a^2)} - c$ (2)

Unit 2 **3** Are these statements true or false? Tick the boxes. If the statement is false, correct it. 🔢
   (a) The sum of three numbers can be expressed by $a + b + c$ True ☐ False ☐ (1)
   (b) The difference between two numbers can be expressed by $p + q$ True ☐ False ☐ (1)
   (c) The product of three numbers can be expressed by $cd + e$ True ☐ False ☐ (1)
   (d) The difference between two numbers, divided by a third number
   can be expressed by $\dfrac{p - q}{r}$ True ☐ False ☐ (1)
   (e) $a(b + c) \equiv ab + ac$ is an identity   True ☐ False ☐ (1)

Unit 2 **4** **(a)** Solve $p - 3 = 0$ 🔢 (1)
   (b) Solve $\dfrac{q}{2} = 4$ (1)
   (c) Solve $3r - 2 = 13$ (2)

Unit 2 **5** **(a)** The next term of a sequence is obtained by the following rule: 🔢
   'Multiply the previous term by 2 and then add 3'.
   The first two terms of the sequence are 2 and 7. Write down the next two terms. (2)
   (b) A different sequence has an nth term of $3n$. The first term is 3. Write down the next
   three terms. (1)
   (c) Work out the nth term of the following sequence:

   2, 5, 8, 11, 14... (2)

Unit 2 **6** **(a)** Factorise $3a - a^2$ 🔢 (1)
   (b) Factorise $49 - b^2$ (1)
   (c) Solve the equation $5 + 3c = 6 - c$ (3)
   (d) Solve $\dfrac{x + 3}{3} - \dfrac{x - 2}{4} = \dfrac{7}{4}$ (4)

Exam practice questions

Unit 2 **7** Show the following on number lines. 📱

    (a) $x < 4$ **(1)**

    (b) $x \geqslant -3$ **(1)**

    (c) $-2 \leqslant x < 1$ **(1)**

    (d) $2x - 1 > 5$ **(2)**

    (e) $4 \geqslant y - 1 > 1$ **(2)**

Unit 2 **8** **(a)** Find the gradient and y-intercept of this straight line. 📱

        $2y = -5x$ **(2)**

    (b) Are these lines parallel?

        $2y = 4x + 1$ $y = \dfrac{6x + 4}{3}$ $y = x - 2$ **(3)**

Unit 2 **9** Simplify: 📱

    (a) $\dfrac{(2x - 1)}{4} - \dfrac{(x - 3)}{3}$ **(2)**

    (b) $\dfrac{3a - 1}{4a + 3} + \dfrac{4}{5}$ **(2)**

    (c) $\dfrac{5}{2b - 3} + \dfrac{2}{b + 2}$ **(2)**

Unit 2 **10** **(a)** In a cricket match, one of the batsman hit a sixes, b fours and c single runs. 📱

        Write an expression for the number of runs the batsman scored.   **(2)**

    (b) A worker has to pay income tax of p pence in every pound he earns.

        His income is £P, of which £Q is tax free.

        Write a formula for the amount of tax (£T) he has to pay.   **(2)**

    (c) Write down an equation for three consecutive numbers that add up to 48.   **(2)**

Unit 2 **11** **(a)** Find two numbers that add up to 27 and have a difference of 3. 📱   **(2)**

    (b) A concert is arranged to raise funds for a charity.

        500 tickets are sold at two prices: £5 and £8.

        The income from the more expensive tickets is £100 more than that from the

        less expensive tickets. How many of each price tickets were sold?   **(4)**

Unit 3 **12** Solve:

    (a) $\dfrac{3}{x + 2} + \dfrac{1}{x - 1} = 2$ giving your answer to 3 s.f.   **(6)**

    (b) $5x + y = 14$

        $2x - y = 7$ **(5)**

    (c) $2x^2 - 5x - 12 = 0$ **(3)**

Unit 3 **13** Using a table of coordinates for $-2 \leqslant x \leqslant 2$ draw a graph of $y = x^3 - 4$ **(4)**

Exam practice questions

Unit 3 **14** Use this grid to solve these simultaneous equations graphically. **(6)**

$x + y = 3$

$3x + 2y = 7$

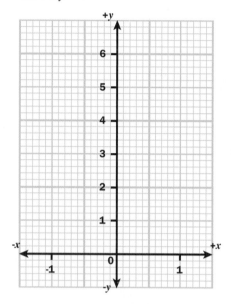

Unit 3 **15** Here is the graph of $y = f(x)$.

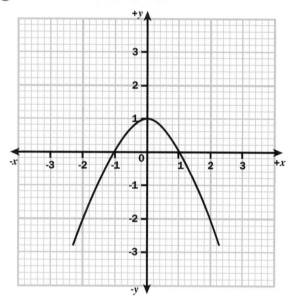

The maximum point has coordinates (0, 1). Find the coordinates of the maximum point of:

(a) $y = f(x) + 2$

(b) $y = f(x) - 2$

(c) $y = f(x + 2)$

(d) $y = f(x - 2)$ **(5)**

4 Geometry and measures

The following topics are covered in this chapter:

- **Angles**
- **Triangles**
- **Polygons**
- **Quadrilaterals**
- **Trigonometry**
- **Circles**
- **3D shapes**
- **Transformations**
- **Scales**
- **Converting measures**
- **Estimating**
- **Bearings**
- **Constructions and loci**
- **Area and perimeter**
- **Volume and surface area**
- **Effect of enlargement**
- **Vectors**

4.1 Angles

LEARNING SUMMARY	After studying this section, you should be able to understand: • facts about angles • angle properties

Facts about angles

Unit 1   *X*
Unit 2   *X*
Unit 3   ✓

KEY POINT

An angle is the amount of turning measured in degrees.

Angle	Fact	Diagram
Angles at a point	Add up to 360° Called a full revolution. $a + b + c + d = 360°$	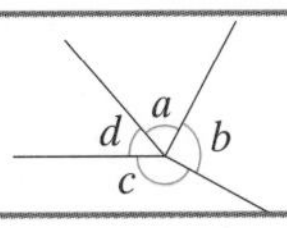
Acute angles	Lie between 0° and 90° $0° < a < 90°$	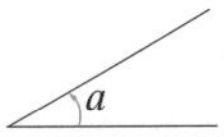
Obtuse angles	Lie between 90° and 180° $90° < a < 180°$	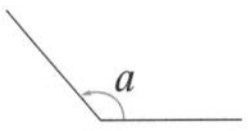
Reflex angles	Lie between 180° and 360° $180° < a < 360°$	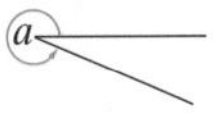
Right angles	Equal 90°	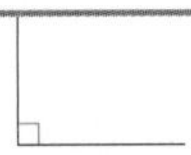
Complementary angles	Add up to 90° $a + b = 90°$	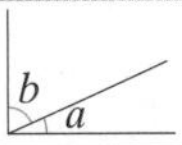
Adjacent angles on a straight line	Add up to 180° These angles are called supplementary angles. $a + b + c = 180°$	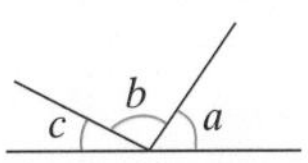

Angle properties

Unit 1   ✗
Unit 2   ✗
Unit 3   ✓

- When two straight lines intersect, the opposite angles are equal. These are called vertically opposite angles.

  $a = c$ $b = d$

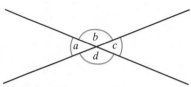

- When a line crosses parallel lines:

  $x = y$ ← Corresponding angles

  $w = y$ ← Alternate angles

  $v + w = 180°$ ← Allied or interior angles

> Parallel lines are denoted by sets of arrows.

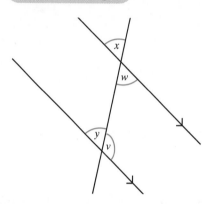

PROGRESS CHECK

Diagrams not drawn to scale

🔲 **Without using a calculator**

1. What type of angle is
   (a) 35°   **(b)** 210°   **(c)** 87°   **(d)** 97°

2. Find the missing angles.

3. Find the missing angles giving reasons.

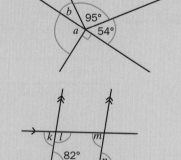

1. (a) Acute (b) Reflex (c) Acute (d) Obtuse   2. $a = 90°$ $b = 31°$
3. $k = 82°$ (alternate angles) $l = 98°$ (allied angles or on a straight line)
$m = 82°$ (corresponding angles) $n = 82°$ (alternate angles)

4.2 Triangles

LEARNING SUMMARY	After studying this section, you should be able to understand: ● notation used in triangles ● types of triangles ● Pythagoras' theorem ● congruency and similarity

Notation used in triangles

Unit 1	✗
Unit 2	✗
Unit 3	✓

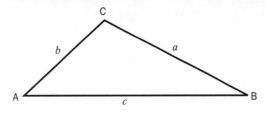

Angles are written as ∠ A or ∠ BAC   ← This is sometimes seen as Å or BÂC

∠ BAC is the angle where AB meets AC.

> You will often find that a small letter is written in the angle for convenience.

Sides are usually written using their endpoints AB, BC, CA.

Sometimes a small letter is used where '*a*' is the side opposite ∠ A.

Triangle ABC may be written as ABC.

Types of triangles

Unit 1	✗
Unit 2	✗
Unit 3	✓

KEY POINT

A triangle is a polygon with three sides and three angles that add up to 180°

> Denote equal length sides by short cross lines.
>
> A triangle with three acute angles is called an acute-angled triangle.
>
> A triangle with an obtuse angle is called an obtuse-angled triangle.
>
> Remember, there can only be one obtuse angle because the angles in a triangle add up to 180°

Triangle	Fact	Diagram
Scalene triangle	Three different sides and three different angles. $a + b + c = 180°$	
Equilateral triangle	Three equal sides and three equal angles. As the three equal angles add up to 180°, they each equal 60°	
Isosceles triangle	Two equal sides. The angles opposite these sides are equal.	
Right-angled triangle	Has an angle of 90° The side opposite the right angle is called the **hypotenuse**.	Hypotenuse

Exterior angle of a triangle

> **KEY POINT**
>
> The exterior angle of a triangle is equal to the sum of the opposite two angles.

$x + y + z = 180°$

$a + z = 180°$

$\therefore a = x + y$

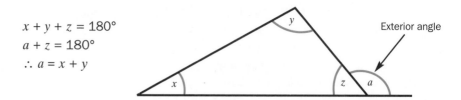

Exterior angle

Pythagoras' theorem

Unit 1   ✗
Unit 2   ✗
Unit 3   ✓

> **KEY POINT**
>
> **Pythagoras' theorem** states that in a right-angled triangle, the square on the hypotenuse is equal to the sum of the squares on the other two sides.
>
> **$BC^2 = AC^2 + AB^2$**
>
> or $a^2 = b^2 + c^2$

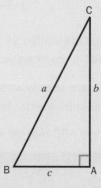

Pythagoras' theorem can be used...

- to find the length of a side when you are given the length of the other two sides
- to prove that a triangle is right-angled
- to find the length of a line segment
- in 3D problems.

Finding a missing side of a right-angled triangle

> **Examples**
>
> **1.** Find the hypotenuse:
>
> $BC^2 = AC^2 + AB^2$
>
> $\quad = 10^2 + 24^2$
>
> $\quad = 100 + 576 = 676$
>
> $\therefore BC = \sqrt{676} = 26\text{cm}$
>
>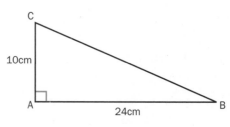
>
> Not drawn to scale

Do not forget to square root to find the answer.

2. Find the missing side:
$$AB^2 + BC^2 = AC^2$$
$$AB^2 = AC^2 - BC^2$$
$$= 12^2 - 8^2$$
$$= 144 - 64 = 80$$
$$\therefore AB = \sqrt{80} = 8.94cm \ (2 \ d.p.)$$

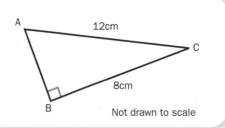

Not drawn to scale

Proving that a triangle is right-angled

Unless a triangle is drawn accurately, do not assume that an angle is a right angle.

Take the longest side to be the hypotenuse.

If the sides of the triangle are in the ratios

3 : 4 : 5   5 : 12 : 13
8 : 15 :17   7 : 24 : 25

you will find they are right-angled triangles.

The symbol ≠ means 'not equal'.

Example

Diagrams not drawn to scale

Are these triangles right-angled?

(a)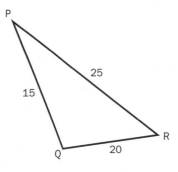

(b)

Use Pythagoras' theorem for each triangle. If it does not work, the triangle has no right angle.

(a) $BC^2 = 15^2 = 225$
$AB^2 + AC^2 = 8^2 + 6^2$
$\qquad \qquad = 64 + 36 = 100$
$BC^2 \neq AB^2 + AC^2$
$\therefore$ ABC is not right-angled.

(b) $PR^2 = 25^2 = 625$
$PQ^2 + QR^2 = 15^2 + 20^2$
$\qquad \qquad = 225 + 400 = 625$
$PR^2 = PQ^2 + QR^2$
$\therefore$ PQR is right-angled.

Finding the length of a line segment

> **KEY POINT**
>
> A **line segment** is part of a line. This may be given by the coordinates of its ends.

You can use Pythagoras' theorem to find the length of a line segment and the coordinates of the midpoint of a line segment.

> **KEY POINT**
>
> The x-coordinate of the midpoint of a line segment is given by the average of the x-coordinates of the two endpoints.
>
> The y-coordinate of the midpoint of a line segment is given by the average of the y-coordinates of the two endpoints.
>
> The average is found by adding the coordinates together and dividing by two.

Example

(a) Find the length of the line segments AB and PQ.
(b) What are the coordinates of their midpoints (M_a and M_b)?

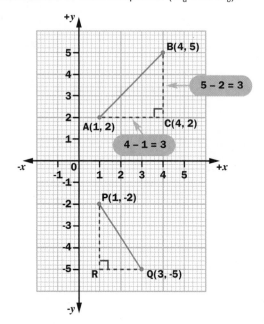

Form a right-angled triangle using the line segment as the hypotenuse.
Write out Pythagoras' theorem and then substitute in the values.

(a) $AB^2 = AC^2 + BC^2$ $PQ^2 = PR^2 + RQ^2$
   $AB^2 = 3^2 + 3^2 = 9 + 9$ $PQ^2 = (-3)^2 + 2^2 = 9 + 4$
      $= 18$ $= 13$
   $\therefore AB = \sqrt{18} = 4.2$ (1 d.p.) $PQ = \sqrt{13} = 3.6$ (1 d.p.)

(b) Endpoints of AB are A(1, 2) and B(4, 5)
   Endpoints of PQ are P(1, -2) and Q(3, -5)
   Midpoint of AB: $x = (1 + 4) \div 2 = 2.5$; $y = (2 + 5) \div 2 = 3.5$
   Midpoint of PQ: $x = (1 + 3) \div 2 = 2$; $y = (-2 + -5) \div 2 = -3.5$
   M_a is the point (2.5, 3.5)
   M_b is the point (2, -3.5)

3D problems

Pythagoras' theorem in 3D problems can be found on higher level papers.

Draw out the triangles. This will show you exactly what you are looking for.

You may not need to square root the first stage if you just need the square in the second stage.

Example

Diagrams not drawn to scale

Find the lengths of the diagonals BD and BE.

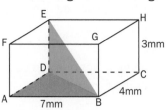
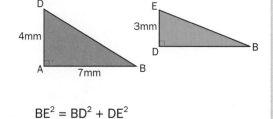

$BD^2 = AB^2 + AD^2$ $BE^2 = BD^2 + DE^2$
   $= 7^2 + 4^2$ $= 65 + 3^2$
   $= 49 + 16$ $= 65 + 9$
   $= 65$ $= 74$
$\therefore BD = \sqrt{65} = 8.06$mm (3 s.f.) $BE = \sqrt{74} = 8.6$mm (1 d.p)

Congruency and similarity

Unit 1   ✗
Unit 2   ✗
Unit 3   ✓

Congruent triangles

> **KEY POINT**
>
> Triangles that are exactly the same shape and size are said to be **congruent**. This also applies to other shapes.

Triangles can be proved to be congruent if...

> The side and angles must be in the same position in both triangles.

- two angles and a corresponding side are equal (AAS)

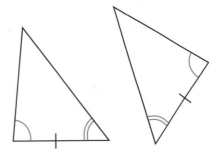

- two sides and the included angle are equal (SAS)

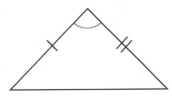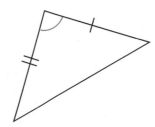

- three sides are equal (SSS)

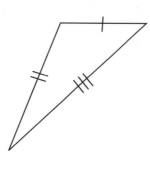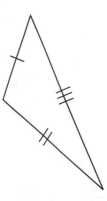

- the hypotenuse and one side are equal (in right-angled triangles) (RHS)

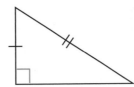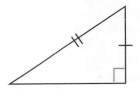

Similar triangles

> **KEY POINT**
>
> Triangles that have the same angles, but different length sides, are said to be **similar**. The lengths of the sides are in the same ratio or proportion. This also applies to other shapes.

Similar shapes can be found on higher level papers.

If two triangles are similar, one is an enlargement of the other. The lengths will enlarge by a given scale factor.

Example

Find PQ, XZ, YZ.

Diagrams not drawn to scale

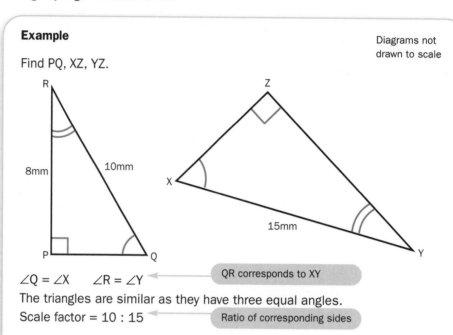

$\angle Q = \angle X \qquad \angle R = \angle Y$ ← QR corresponds to XY

The triangles are similar as they have three equal angles.

Scale factor = 10 : 15 ← Ratio of corresponding sides

To find PQ, use Pythagoras' theorem:

$PQ^2 = QR^2 - PR^2 = 10^2 - 8^2 = 100 - 64 = 36$

$\therefore PQ = \sqrt{36} = 6mm$

The corresponding sides are:

$$\frac{PQ}{XZ} = \frac{PR}{YZ} = \frac{10}{15}$$ ← Sides are in same proportion

To find XZ:

$$\frac{PQ}{XZ} = \frac{10}{15}$$

$$\frac{6}{XZ} = \frac{2}{3}$$ ← Substitute and cancel by 5

$3 \times 6 = 2 \times XZ$

$18 \div 2 = XZ$

$\therefore XZ = 9mm$

In this example, you are finding a side on a larger triangle, so use $\frac{15}{10}$ as the scale factor.

If you were finding a side on a smaller triangle, you would use $\frac{10}{15}$ as the scale factor.

To find YZ:

$$YZ = PR \times \frac{15}{10}$$ ← Scale factor for longer side

$$= 8 \times \frac{3}{2}$$ ← Cancel by 5

$\therefore YZ = 12mm$

PROGRESS CHECK

Diagrams not drawn to scale

1 Find the missing angles.

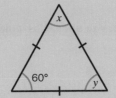
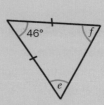
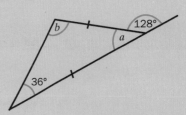

2 Use Pythagoras' theorem to find the missing sides in EFG.
(a) Find g when $e = 4$, $f = 7.5$
(b) Find e when $f = 18$, $g = 30$
(c) Find f when $e = 1.6$, $g = 2$

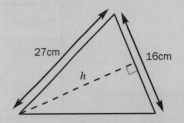

3 Use Pythagoras' theorem to find whether these triangles are right-angled.
(a) $e = 10$, $f = 24$, $g = 26$
(b) $e = 4.4$, $f = 3$, $g = 5.5$
(c) $e = 7.2$, $f = 3$, $g = 7.8$

4 What is the perpendicular height of this isosceles triangle?

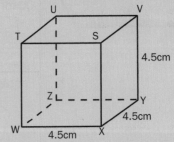

5 A cube has sides 4.5cm.
Find the length of the diagonal UX.

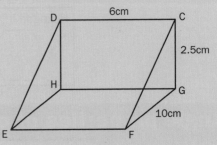

6 A wooden door wedge has a diagonal stripe painted on it.
How long is the stripe DF?

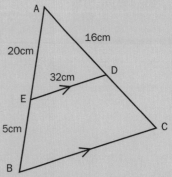

7 Find AC and BC.

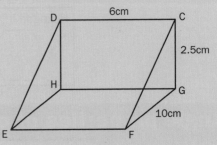

1. (a) $x = y = 60°$ (b) $e = f = 67°$ (c) $a = 52°$, $b = 92°$ 2. (a) 8.5 (b) 24 (c) 1.2
3. (a) Yes [$10^2 = 24^2 = 100 + 576 = 676 = g^2$] (b) No [$4.4^2 + 3^2 = 19.36 + 9 = 28.36 \neq g^2$]
(c) Yes [$7.2^2 + 3^2 = 51.84 + 9 = 60.84 = g^2$] 4. 25.8cm (3 s.f.) 5. 7.79cm (3 s.f.)
6. 11.9cm (3 s.f.) 7. AC = 20cm, BC = 40cm

4.3 Polygons

LEARNING SUMMARY

After studying this section, you should be able to understand:
- types of polygons
- angle properties of polygons
- tessellations

Types of polygons

Unit 1   ✗
Unit 2   ✗
Unit 3   ✓

KEY POINT

A **polygon** is a straight-sided plane figure.
Regular polygons have equal sides. Irregular polygons do not.

See 4.2 Triangles and 4.4 Quadrilaterals for properties of these polygons.

Polygon	No. of sides
Triangle	3
Quadrilateral	4
Pentagon	5
Hexagon	6

Polygon	No. of sides
Octagon	8
Nonagon	9
Decagon	10

Angle properties of polygons

Unit 1   ✗
Unit 2   ✗
Unit 3   ✓

KEY POINT

In a polygon, the interior angle + the exterior angle = 180°

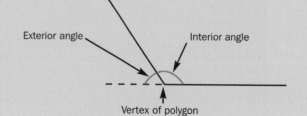

Exterior angle   Interior angle

Vertex of polygon

Exterior angle of a polygon

> **KEY POINT**
>
> For all polygons, the sum of the exterior angles = 360°

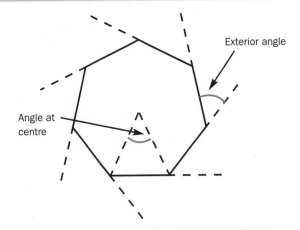

The angle at the centre of a
regular polygon = exterior angle
= 360° ÷ number of sides.

Example

Calculate the exterior angle of a regular pentagon.

A regular pentagon has five sides and five equal exterior angles.
Sum of exterior angles = 360°
Exterior angle = 360° ÷ 5 = 72°

Interior angle of a polygon

To find the interior angle of a regular polygon, find the exterior angle first.

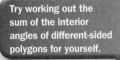

Learn that the number of
lines of symmetry of a
regular polygon is equal
to the number of sides.

Example

Calculate the interior angle of a regular hexagon.

A regular hexagon has six sides and six equal exterior angles.
Exterior angle = 360° ÷ 6 = 60°
Interior angle = 180° − 60° = 120°

To work out the sum of the interior angles of an irregular polygon, first choose
one vertex (corner) of the polygon. Draw the diagonals from that vertex to the
other vertices. This divides the polygon into triangles.

For example:
A seven-sided polygon (heptagon)
has five triangles.

Try working out the
sum of the interior
angles of different-sided
polygons for yourself.

Each triangle has an angle sum of
180°, so sum of interior angles =
5 × 180° = 900°

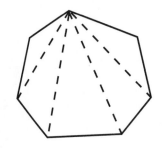

This table shows the sum of the interior angles for different irregular polygons:

Number of sides	Triangles	Sum of interior angles
3	1	1 × 180° = 180°
4	2	2 × 180° = 360°
5	3	3 × 180° = 540°
6	4	4 × 180° = 720°
8	6	6 × 180° = 1080°
9	7	7 × 180° = 1260°
10	8	8 × 180° = 1440°

Notice that the number of triangles is 2 less than the number of sides of the polygon.

∴ sum of interior angles of a polygon = $(n - 2) \times 180°$

where n is the number of sides of a polygon.

Example

Calculate the sum of the interior angles of a nine-sided irregular polygon.

Sum of interior angles $= (9 - 2) \times 180°$ ← Substitute $n = 9$

$= 7 \times 180° = 1260°$

Tessellations

Unit 1 ✗
Unit 2 ✗
Unit 3 ✓

KEY POINT

A **tessellation** is a pattern made from fitting together polygons (usually regular polygons) without leaving gaps.

Tessellations are used for tiling walls and floors.

The points where vertices meet must have a total angle of 360°.

All triangles and quadrilaterals will tessellate.

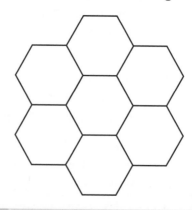

PROGRESS CHECK

1 What is the exterior angle of a regular...
   (a) octagon?   **(b)** nonagon?

2 Calculate the sum of the interior angles of an irregular...
   (a) pentagon.   **(b)** hexagon.

1. (a) 45° (b) 40°   2. (a) 540° (b) 720°

4.4 Quadrilaterals

After studying this section, you should be able to understand:

- angles in a quadrilateral
- properties of quadrilaterals

Angles in a quadrilateral

Unit 1	X
Unit 2	X
Unit 3	✓

KEY POINT

A **quadrilateral** is a polygon with four sides and four angles that add up to 360°.

We can easily prove that the angle sum of a quadrilateral equals 360°.

Divide any quadrilateral into two parts by drawing a diagonal.

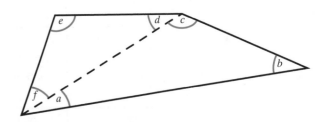

This gives two triangles each of which has an angle sum of 180°

$a + b + c = 180°$

$d + e + f = 180°$

∴ the angle sum of a quadrilateral = $2 \times 180° = 360°$

Example

Find ∠ CBD and ∠ CAD.

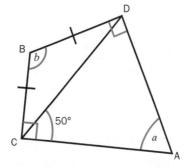

Not drawn to scale

∠ BCD = 90° − 50° = 40°

BCD is isosceles (BC = BD)

so ∠ BCD = ∠ CDB = 40°

∴ ∠ CBD = 180° − (2 × 40°) = 100°

∠ CAD = 360° − (2(90°) + 100°) = 80°

Properties of quadrilaterals

Unit 1   X
Unit 2   X
Unit 3   ✓

It is important to learn how to recognise different quadrilaterals.
This table shows you the properties of different quadrilaterals.

Quadrilateral	Sides	Angles	Diagonals	Symmetry
Square	Four equal and parallel sides	All angles are 90°	Bisect each other at right angles	Four lines of symmetry. Order of rotation 4
Rectangle	Two pairs of equal and parallel sides	All angles are 90°	Bisect each other	Two lines of symmetry. Order of rotation 2
Parallelogram	Two pairs of equal and parallel sides	Opposite angles are equal	Bisect each other	No lines of symmetry. Order of rotation 2
Rhombus	Four equal sides. Two pairs of parallel sides	Opposite angles are equal	Bisect each other at right angles	Two lines of symmetry. Order of rotation 2
Kite	Two pairs of adjacent sides equal	One pair of opposite angles are equal	Cut at right angles; shorter diagonal bisected	One line of symmetry. No rotational symmetry
Arrowhead	Two pairs of adjacent sides are equal	One pair of equal angles	One diagonal	One line of symmetry. No rotational symmetry
Trapezium	One pair of parallel sides	No equal angles	Diagonals different	No lines of symmetry. No rotational symmetry
Isosceles trapezium	One pair of parallel sides. 2nd pair equal sides	Two pairs of equal angles	Two equal diagonals	One line of symmetry. No rotational symmetry

PROGRESS CHECK

Find a, b and c in each quadrilateral.

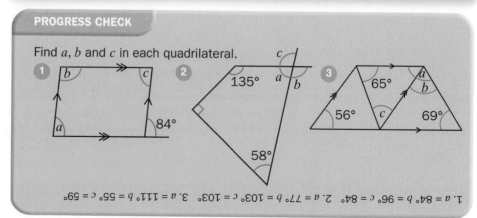

1. $a = 84°$ $b = 96°$ $c = 84°$ 2. $a = 77°$ $b = 77°$ $c = 103°$ 3. $a = 111°$ $b = 55°$ $c = 59°$

4.5 Trigonometry

LEARNING SUMMARY

After studying this section, you should be able to understand:

- trigonometric ratios
- finding trigonometric ratios of any angle
- area of a triangle using trigonometric formula
- sine and cosine rules

Trigonometric ratios

Unit 1	✗
Unit 2	✗
Unit 3	✓

Trigonometry shows the relationship between sides and angles in a right-angled triangle. Trigonometry can be used to find the length of sides and sizes of angles in right-angled triangles.

> Trigonometry can be found on higher level papers.

> If only sides are mentioned in the question, use Pythagoras' theorem; if angles are mentioned in the question as well, use trigonometry.

KEY POINT

Learn these ratios:

$$\sin \theta = \frac{\text{Opposite}}{\text{Hypotenuse}}$$

$$\cos \theta = \frac{\text{Adjacent}}{\text{Hypotenuse}}$$

$$\tan \theta = \frac{\text{Opposite}}{\text{Adjacent}}$$

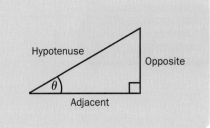

There are two ways to use these ratios.

Finding a side

Example

Find AB.

$$\frac{AB}{8} = \sin 26°$$ ← Use sin = $\frac{\text{Opposite}}{\text{Hypotenuse}}$

$$AB = 8 \times \sin 26°$$
$$= 3.5069$$
$$AB = 3.51\text{cm (3 s.f.)}$$

> Check your calculator to find the sin, cos and tan keys.

Not drawn to scale

Finding an angle

Example

Find ∠ BAC.

$$\cos A = \frac{7.3}{18.2}$$ ← Use cos = $\frac{\text{Adjacent}}{\text{Hypotenuse}}$

$$= 0.4011$$ ← Use the cos⁻¹ key on your calculator

$$\angle BAC = 66.4°$$ ← You should usually give an angle to 1 d.p.

> You could cut out the middle step but marks are awarded for giving the correct ratio.

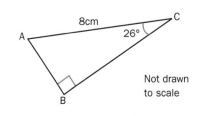

Not drawn to scale

Angles of elevation and depression

KEY POINT

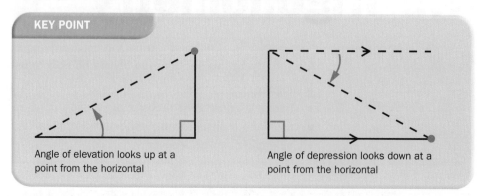

Angle of elevation looks up at a point from the horizontal

Angle of depression looks down at a point from the horizontal

Example   Diagrams not drawn to scale

1. What is the angle of elevation of the top of a tree, 21m high, from a point 25m from the foot of the tree?

> It is a good idea to draw a diagram illustrating the given information.

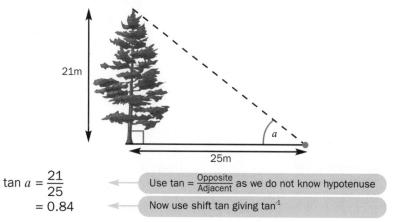

21m

25m

$$\tan a = \frac{21}{25}$$

◄── Use $\tan = \frac{\text{Opposite}}{\text{Adjacent}}$ as we do not know hypotenuse

$$= 0.84$$

◄── Now use shift tan giving $\tan^{-1}$

Angle of elevation (a) = 40° (to nearest degree)

2. A man standing on the top of a cliff 40m high looks at a yacht out at sea. The angle of depression is 22°. How far away from the base of the cliff is the boat? (Assume the cliff meets the ground at 90° and the horizontal and ground are parallel for the purposes of the calculation.)

RS is the distance of the boat from the cliff.

∠ RST = 22° (alternate angles)

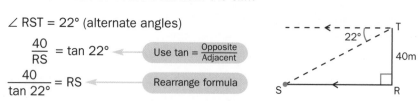

$$\frac{40}{RS} = \tan 22°$$ ◄── Use $\tan = \frac{\text{Opposite}}{\text{Adjacent}}$

$$\frac{40}{\tan 22°} = RS$$ ◄── Rearrange formula

Distance of boat (RS) = 99m (to nearest whole metre)

Finding trigonometric ratios of any angle

Unit 1 ✗
Unit 2 ✗
Unit 3 ✓

This diagram shows a circle with radius, r, with centre at the origin. The point P, which has coordinates (x, y), can be anywhere on the circumference.

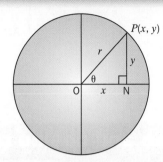

KEY POINT

Using the right-angled triangle NOP:

$$\sin \theta = \frac{NP}{OP}, = \frac{y}{r} \qquad \cos \theta = \frac{ON}{OP} = \frac{x}{r} \qquad \tan \theta = \frac{NP}{ON} = \frac{y}{x}$$

The circle can be divided up into quadrants like this:

When θ has a value of 100° it is in the 2nd quadrant

90°

2nd quadrant | 1st quadrant

180°

3rd quadrant | 4th quadrant

0°

270°

When θ has a value of 340° it is in the 4th quadrant

As P moves round the circumference of the circle, so x and y can be negative or positive depending on the value of θ. For example, when θ is in the 2nd quadrant, x is negative, but y is positive.

This means that in the 2nd quadrant, $\sin \theta = \frac{y}{r}$ is positive, but $\cos \theta = \frac{x}{r}$ is negative (by convention we always assume that the radius is positive).

This table shows whether the angles are positive or negative in each quadrant:

Quadrant	1st	2nd	3rd	4th
$\sin \theta$	positive	positive	negative	negative
$\cos \theta$	positive	negative	negative	positive
$\tan \theta$	positive	negative	positive	negative

Area of a triangle using trigonometric formula

Unit 1 ✗
Unit 2 ✗
Unit 3 ✓

KEY POINT

The area of any triangle with two given sides and the angle between them can be found by using the formula:

Area $= \frac{1}{2} ab \sin C$

or $\quad = \frac{1}{2} bc \sin A$

or $\quad = \frac{1}{2} ac \sin B$

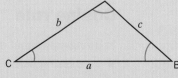

The formula you use depends on the information given.

Example

Find the area of $\triangle$ ABC

Area $= \dfrac{1}{2} bc \sin A$

$= \dfrac{1}{2} \times 7.2 \times 8 \times \sin 105°$

$= 27.8\text{mm}^2$ (3 s.f.)

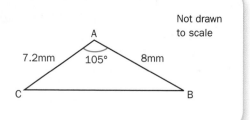

Not drawn to scale

Sine and cosine rules

Unit 1   ✗
Unit 2   ✗
Unit 3   ✓

Sine rule

In triangles without a right angle, use the sine rule to find:
- a missing side if you know two angles and an opposite side
- a missing angle if you know an angle and two sides.

> Remember, for right-angled triangles, use Pythagoras' Theorem to find a missing side and trigonometric ratios to find a missing side or angle.

KEY POINT

The sine rule is:

$$\dfrac{a}{\sin A} = \dfrac{b}{\sin B} = \dfrac{c}{\sin C}$$

or

$$\dfrac{\sin A}{a} = \dfrac{\sin B}{b} = \dfrac{\sin C}{c}$$

The triangle might use different letters such as PQR or CDE. Adjust the formula accordingly.

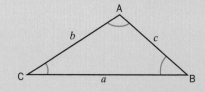

Examples

Diagrams not drawn to scale

1. Find AB.

   AB is side c opposite $\angle$ C

   $$\dfrac{c}{\sin C} = \dfrac{a}{\sin A}$$

   Use the appropriate part of the sine rule

   $$\dfrac{c}{\sin 36°} = \dfrac{2.5}{\sin 77°}$$

   $$c = \dfrac{2.5 \times \sin 36°}{\sin 77°}$$

   $\therefore$ AB $= 1.51$m (3 s.f.)

2. Find $\angle$ QPR.

   $$\dfrac{\sin P}{p} = \dfrac{\sin R}{r}$$

   $$\dfrac{\sin P}{16} = \dfrac{\sin 40°}{14}$$

   $$\sin P = \dfrac{16 \times \sin 40°}{14}$$

   $$= 0.734\,614\,411$$

   Use the $\sin^{-1}$ key on your calculator

   $\angle$ QPR $= 47.3°$

> Remember angles are given to 1 d.p. where necessary.

Cosine rule

In triangles without a right angle, use the cosine rule to find:
- a missing side if you know two sides and the included angle
- a missing angle if you know three sides.

KEY POINT

The cosine rule is:
$$a^2 = b^2 + c^2 - 2bc \cos A$$
or $b^2 = a^2 + c^2 - 2ac \cos B$
or $c^2 = a^2 + b^2 - 2ab \cos C$

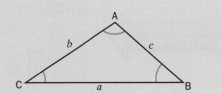

Examples   Diagrams not drawn to scale

1. Find AB. ← AB is side c
   $c^2 = a^2 + b^2 - 2ab \cos C$ ← Adjusted cosine rule
   $\quad = 9^2 + 11^2 - 2(9 \times 11 \times \cos 60°)$
   $\quad = 81 + 121 - (2 \times 99 \times 0.5)$
   $\quad = 202 - 99 = 103$
   $c \quad = \sqrt{103} = 10.148\,89$
   $\therefore$ AB = 10.1cm (3 s.f.)

2. Find $\angle$ ABC.
   $b^2 = a^2 + c^2 - 2ac \cos B$ ← Adjusted cosine rule
   $\cos B = \dfrac{a^2 + c^2 - b^2}{2ac}$

   $\cos B = \dfrac{8^2 + 7^2 - 5^2}{2 \times 8 \times 7}$

   $\quad = \dfrac{64 + 49 - 25}{112}$

   $\quad = \dfrac{88}{112}$

   $\quad = 0.785\,714\,285$ ← Use the $\cos^{-1}$ key on your calculator
   $\angle$ ABC = 38.2°

> You can rearrange to make cos B the subject of the formula or just substitute and then rearrange.

PROGRESS CHECK   Diagrams not drawn to scale

1 Find the missing sides and angles. Give your answers for sides to 3 s.f. and angles to 1 d.p.

(a)
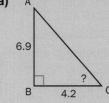

(b)

(c)

(d)
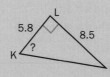

(e)

(f)

2 This is a sketch of a lean-to shed at the side of a house. The sides are at right angles to the ground.

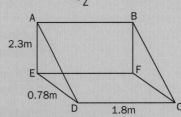

Find:
(a) the angle $\angle$ ADE between the slanting roof and the ground
(b) the length AD of the roof support.
(c) the area of wood needed to build the shed, (include the wall attached to the house and the floor).

It helps to sketch a rough diagram of triangles.

PROGRESS CHECK

③ Find the area of each triangle:
  (a) AC = 11cm, BC = 9cm, ∠ACB = 60°
  (b) AC = 50mm, BC = 24mm, ∠ACB = 93°
  (c) PR = 4.2cm, RQ = 6.3cm, ∠PRQ = 66°
④ **(a)** Find ∠BAC when BC = 11cm, AC = 10cm, AB = 8cm
  (b) Find ∠BCA when AB = 68m, AC = 59m, ∠ABC = 41°
⑤ A man 1.8m tall stands 18m away from a 25m clock tower. Calculate the angle of elevation of the top of the tower from his eyes.
⑥ Are these trigonometric ratios positive or negative?
  (a) sin 290°   **(b)** cos 156°   **(c)** tan 230°

4. (a) 74.4° (b) 49.1° 5. 52.2° 6. (a) Negative (b) Negative (c) Positive
2. (a) 71.3° (b) 2.43m (c) 11.7m² 3. (a) 42.9cm² (b) 599mm² (c) 12.1cm²
1. (a) 58.7° (b) 11.3 (c) 15.0 (d) 55.7° (e) 50.5° (f) 16.8

4.6 Circles

LEARNING SUMMARY

After studying this section, you should be able to understand:

- parts of a circle
- angles in a circle
- chord theorem
- tangents and angles

Parts of a circle

Unit 1	✗
Unit 2	✗
Unit 3	✓

- A **diameter** divides a circle into two semi-circles. If two diameters intersect at right angles, they divide the circle into four quadrants.
- An **arc** is part of the circumference.
- A **segment** is the area between a chord and the circumference.
- A **sector** is a section of a circle between two radii and an arc.
- A **tangent** is a line that just touches a circle at one point.

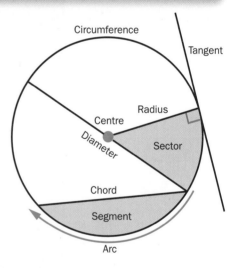

KEY POINT

$$\frac{\text{Circumference}(C)}{\text{Diameter}(d)} = \pi = 3.142 \text{ or } \frac{22}{7} \text{ or approx. } 3$$

Area of circle$(A) = \pi r^2$
Circumference of circle$(C) = \pi d$ or $2\pi r$

Angles in a circle

Unit 1   ✗
Unit 2   ✗
Unit 3   ✓

Circle theorems can be found on higher level papers.

Angle in a semi-circle

> **KEY POINT**
>
> The angle in a semi-circle is always a right angle.

This can be proved as follows:

The angle in a semi-circle is subtended by a diameter at the circumference.

OA = OB = OC ← All radii of a circle

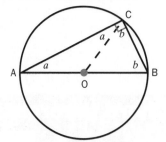

This means that Δ OAC and Δ OBC are isosceles.
In   ABC $a + a + b + b = 180°$
     giving $2(a + b) = 180°$
    ∴ $\angle ACB = a + b = 90°$

Angle at the centre of a circle

> **KEY POINT**
>
> The angle at the centre of a circle is always twice the size of the angle at the circumference subtended by the same arc.

This can be proved as follows:

OA = OB = OC ← All radii of a circle

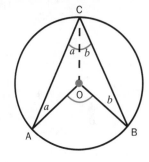

This means that Δ OAC and Δ OBC are isosceles.
Their base angles are equal.
$\angle AOC = 180° - 2a$
$\angle BOC = 180° - 2b$
We know that $\angle AOB + \angle AOC + \angle BOC = 360°$
giving $\angle AOB + (180° - 2a) + (180° - 2b) = 360°$
∴ $\angle AOB = 360° - 180° + 2a - 180° + 2b$
∴ $\angle AOB = 2(a + b) = 2 \times \angle ACB$

Angles in the same segment

> **KEY POINT**
>
> Angles subtended by the same arc, at the circumference, in the same segment are always equal.

We know that the angle at the centre of a circle is twice the size of the angle at the circumference subtended by the same arc. This applies to any angle at the circumference subtended by this arc. In this diagram, the angles marked a are equal.

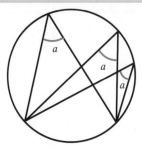

Angles in a cyclic quadrilateral

A **cyclic quadrilateral** is a quadrilateral drawn inside a circle so that all four vertices are on the circumference of the circle.

KEY POINT

The opposite angles of a cyclic quadrilateral add up to 180°.
The exterior angle of a cyclic quadrilateral equals the opposite interior angle.

This can be proved as follows:

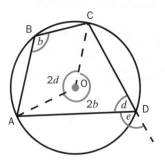

If we mark the centre of the circle (O) and sketch in the radii OA and OC, we know that the angle at the centre is twice the angle at the circumference. We also know that
$2b + 2d = 360°$ or $b + d = 180°$

If we extend CD to form the exterior angle (e) we know that $d + e = 180°$

$\therefore b = e$

Chord theorem

Unit 1	✗
Unit 2	✗
Unit 3	✓

KEY POINT

A line from the centre of a circle to the midpoint of a chord is perpendicular to the chord.

This can be proved as follows:

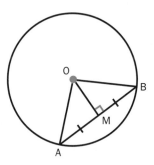

A perpendicular line is drawn from the centre (O) to the midpoint (M) of a chord AB.

In OAM and OBM:
AM = MB
OA = OB ⟵ Radii of circle
OM is the same for both triangles
∴ the triangles are congruent (SSS) so
$\angle$ OMA = $\angle$ OMB = 180° ÷ 2 = 90°

Tangents and angles

Unit 1	✗
Unit 2	✗
Unit 3	✓

KEY POINT

A tangent to a circle is perpendicular to a radius at the point.

Proving this is just an extension of the chord theorem. Draw a chord, then parallel chords, until you get a tangent.

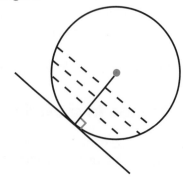

Two tangents drawn to a circle from the same point are equal.
The line drawn from this point, through the centre of the circle, bisects the angle between the tangents. This line bisects the chord joining the points of contact, at right angles.

AB = AC

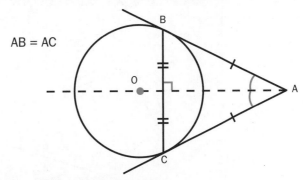

Alternate segment theorem

The angle between a chord and a tangent at the point where it touches the circle equals any angle subtended by that chord in the alternate segment.

This can be proved as follows:

If AC is a diameter $\angle$ ABC = 90°

Angle in semi-circle

$\angle$ OAB + $\angle$ ABC + $\angle$ OCB = 180°

Angle sum of a triangle

so $\angle$ OAB + $\angle$ OCB = 90°
$\angle$ OCT = $\angle$ OCB + $\angle$ BCT = 90°

Tangent meeting radius

this means that $\angle$ BCT = $\angle$ OAB

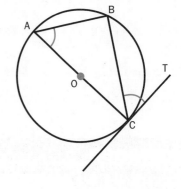

From the angles in the same segment theorem, this will be true for any position of A.

Diagrams not drawn to scale

📱 **Without using a calculator**

Find the missing angles in each of these diagrams.

1 **(a)**   **(b)**

(c)   **(d)**

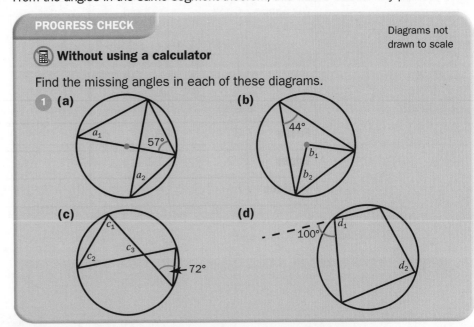

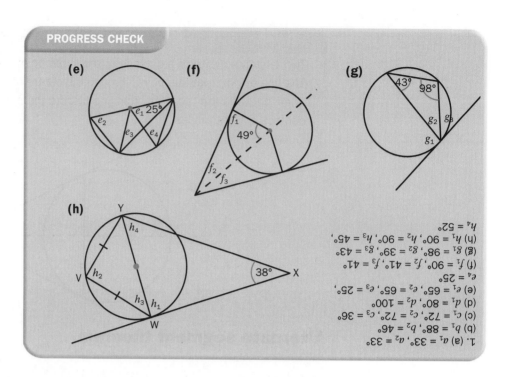

PROGRESS CHECK

1. (a) $a_1 = 33°$, $a_2 = 33°$
(b) $b_1 = 88°$, $b_2 = 46°$
(c) $c_1 = 72°$, $c_2 = 72°$, $c_3 = 36°$
(d) $d_1 = 80°$, $d_2 = 100°$
(e) $e_1 = 65°$, $e_2 = 65°$, $e_3 = 25°$, $e_4 = 25°$
(f) $f_1 = 90°$, $f_2 = 41°$, $f_3 = 41°$
(g) $g_1 = 98°$, $g_2 = 39°$, $g_3 = 43°$
(h) $h_1 = 90°$, $h_2 = 90°$, $h_3 = 45°$, $h_4 = 52°$

4.7 3D shapes

	After studying this section, you should be able to understand:
LEARNING SUMMARY	• 3D shapes • isometric drawing • nets • plans and elevations • 3D coordinates

3D shapes

Unit 1	✗
Unit 2	✗
Unit 3	✓

Plane shapes have two dimensions (2D).
Solid shapes have three dimensions (3D).

For example, a square is a plane shape, but a cube is a solid shape.

3D Shape	Cube	Cuboid	Cylinder	Sphere	Cone
				(A hemisphere is $\frac{1}{2}$ a sphere)	
Faces	6	6	3	1	2
Edges	12	12	2	0	1
Vertices	8	8	0	0	1

There are two more types of 3D shapes:
- **Prisms** take their name from the polygon shape of their uniform cross-section. For example, this diagram is a triangular prism.

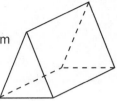

- **Pyramids** take their name from the polygon shape of their base. The perpendicular height is measured from the vertex to the base. A pyramid with four triangular faces is called a **tetrahedron**.

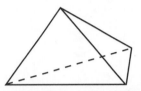

Nets

Unit 1   ✗
Unit 2   ✗
Unit 3   ✓

A 3D solid shape can be constructed from a **net**. The net is the solid shape opened flat.

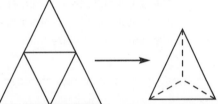

3D coordinates

Unit 1   ✗
Unit 2   ✗
Unit 3   ✓

A solid figure can also be drawn using **3D coordinates**.

3D coordinates can be found on higher level papers.

KEY POINT

Draw a 2D figure using 2D coordinates on two axes x and y. A point has the coordinates (x, y).

Draw a 3D figure using 3D coordinates on three axes x, y, z. A point has the coordinates (x, y, z).

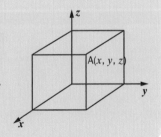

Example

Shape ABCDEFGH is a cube.

(a) How long is a side?

A side is 4 units. ← Read off the axes

(b) What are the coordinates of B, E, F and H?

B (4, 4, 0) ← Read coordinate off each axis in turn

E (4, 0, 4)

F (4, 4, 4)

H (0, 0, 4)

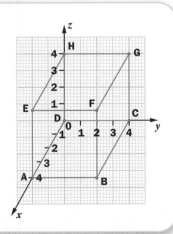

Isometric drawing

Unit 1   *X*
Unit 2   *X*
Unit 3   ✓

Isometric paper has dots or triangles. This enables you to draw solid figures.

Here is a drawing of a cuboid on three different types of paper:

Graph paper

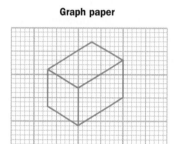

Triangular isometric paper

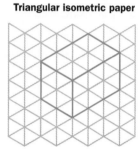

Dotted isometric paper

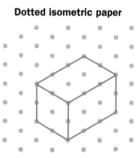

Plans and elevations

Unit 1   *X*
Unit 2   *X*
Unit 3   ✓

> **KEY POINT**
>
> Viewing a solid figure from above is a **plan**.
> Viewing a solid figure from the front is a **front elevation**.
> Viewing a solid figure from the side is a **side elevation**.

In this example it does not matter which side is viewed, but sometimes it does. Read the question carefully.

These types of drawings are used in designing buildings. For example:

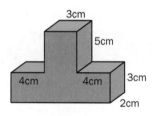

Plan

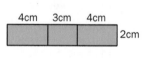

Front elevation

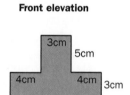

Side elevation

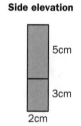

> **PROGRESS CHECK**
>
> 🖩 **Without using a calculator**
>
> 1. Fill the gaps in this table.
>
> | Faces | Edges | Vertices | Shape |
> |-------|-------|----------|-------|
> | 5 | 9 | | Prism (triangular) |
> | | | 8 | Cube |
> | 4 | | 4 | Tetrahedron |
> | 1 | 0 | 0 | |
>
> 2. Draw the net for
>   **(a)** a cylinder   **(b)** a square-based pyramid

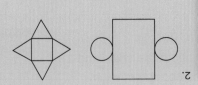
4.8 Transformations

LEARNING SUMMARY

After studying this section, you should be able to understand:

- types of transformations

Types of transformations

Unit 1	✗
Unit 2	✗
Unit 3	✓

A **transformation** moves a shape. It may or may not change size.

Reflection

KEY POINT

Reflection of a shape about a line produces the mirror image of the shape. The line is called the mirror line. A reflection is described by giving the line of symmetry, sometimes as an equation.

Example

Reflect shape ABCDEF in the x-axis and in the y-axis.

Note that the reflected shape remains the same distance from the line of symmetry as was the original shape. The reflected shape and the original shape are congruent, i.e. the same shape and size.

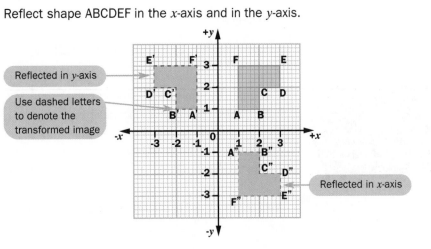

Reflected in y-axis

Use dashed letters to denote the transformed image

Reflected in x-axis

Rotation

> **KEY POINT**
>
> **Rotation** of a shape about a centre, or point, of rotation changes its position but not its size. The angle, centre and direction of rotation must be given.

Example

Rotate shape A, through a right angle, anticlockwise about the origin and 180° clockwise, also about the origin.

Draw a line from the centre of rotation to each vertex of the shape.
Measure the given angle in the given direction from the line for each vertex.
Connect the rotated vertices to give the rotated shape.

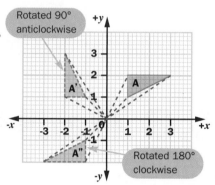

> Note that the rotated shape remains the same size as the original. The rotated shape and the original shape are congruent.

Finding the centre of rotation

If the rotated shape is given and you are asked to find the centre of rotation, follow these steps:

1. Join a corresponding pair of vertices (original and rotated).
2. Construct the perpendicular bisector of this joining line (see page 169).
3. Repeat for another pair of vertices.
4. The two perpendicular bisectors cross at the centre of rotation.

Translation

> **KEY POINT**
>
> **Translation** is when every point of a line or shape moves the same distance in the same direction. The movement is described by a **column vector**.

Example

Translate △ ABC by the column vector $\begin{pmatrix} 4 \\ 3 \end{pmatrix}$

This means move the shape 4 units in a positive horizontal direction and 3 units in a positive vertical direction, i.e. move each vertex 4 units to the right and 3 units upwards.
Label these A', B', C'.
Join A' B' C'.
A' B' C' is the translated triangle.

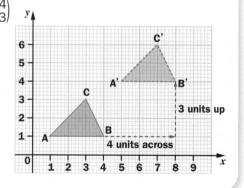

> Note that the translated shape remains the same size as the original. The translated shape and the original shape are congruent.

Enlargement

> **KEY POINT**
>
> **Enlargement** of a shape is when every length is multiplied by the same scale factor.
> - If a scale factor > 1 the shape enlarges.
> - If a scale factor = 1 the shape stays the same size.
> - If 0 < scale factor < 1 the shape reduces in size.
> - If a scale factor < 0 the enlarged shape is upside down on the other side of the centre of enlargement.

Example

Using centre of enlargement O, enlarge △ ABC by scale factor

(a) 3 **(b)** $\frac{1}{2}$ **(c)** -2

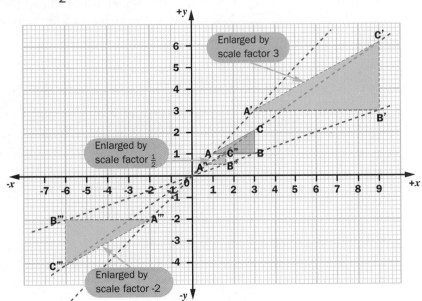

The enlarged shape and the original shape are similar.

Draw a dotted line from O through each vertex A, B, C.

Mark A', B', C' on the dotted lines so that OA' = 3 × OA, OB' = 3 × OB, OC' = 3 × OC

You should find that A'B' = 3 × AB, B'C' = 3 × BC, C'A' = 3 × CA

Join A' B' C' to form the enlarged triangle.

Repeat the process with scale factors $\frac{1}{2}$ and -2.

Finding the centre of enlargement

The centre of enlargement can be any point, not just the origin.

If the enlarged shape is given and you are asked to find the centre of enlargement and scale factor, follow these steps:

1️⃣ Draw dotted lines through two pairs of corresponding vertices.

2️⃣ The centre of enlargement is where these lines cross.

$$\text{Scale factor} = \frac{\text{length of one side of enlarged shape}}{\text{length of corresponding side of original shape}}$$

Combined transformations

Combined transformations can be found on higher level papers.

Two or more transformations may be performed on a shape. The combined effect may be the same as a single transformation.

PROGRESS CHECK

Without using a calculator

1. Plot and join these points to form a shape:

   A (3, 4); B (2, 2); C (4, 2); A (3, 4)

   (a) What shape do they make?

   (b) Reflect the shape in the x-axis and label it RE.

   (c) Rotate shape RE clockwise through 180° about the origin. Label it RO.

   (d) Translate shape RO by vector $\begin{pmatrix} 1 \\ -3 \end{pmatrix}$

   (e) What transformation would move the original shape to RO?

2. Plot and join these points to form a shape:

   P (4, 2), Q (5, 2), R (5, 3), S (6, 3), T (6, 5), U (5, 5), V (5, 6), W (4, 6), P (4, 2)

   Using centre of enlargement (-2, -2) transform the shape by scale factor $\frac{1}{2}$.

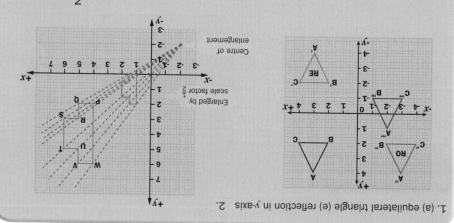

1. (a) equilateral triangle (e) reflection in y-axis 2.

4.9 Scales

After studying this section, you should be able to understand:

- maps and scale drawing
- instrument scales

Maps and scale drawing

Unit 1	✗
Unit 2	✗
Unit 3	✓

Maps and plans have to be drawn to scale to enable large distances to be shown on a page.

Maps

KEY POINT

Maps are drawn to scale $1 : n$ where n is the distance represented by 1cm.

Examples

Four towns C, D, H and J are in the same area. The distances between town G and these towns are shown on a map with scale $1 : 1\,000\,000$.

(a) On the map, G → C = 6.3cm. What is the actual distance between towns G and C?

(b) The actual distance between G → H = 21.04km. What is the map distance between towns G and H?

(a) G → C = 6.3cm

Actual distance $= 6.3 \times 1\,000\,000$ ← Multiply by scale factor

$= 6\,300\,000$cm

$= 63\,000$m   ← Divide by 100 as 100cm = 1m

$= 63$km   ← Divide by 1000 as 1000m = 1km

(b) G → H = 21.04km

Map distance $= \dfrac{21.04 \times 100\,000}{1\,000\,000}$ ← Multiply by 100 000 to change km to cm

← Divide by scale factor

$= 2.104$cm

$= 2.1$cm (1 d.p.)

> 1 d.p. is probably the most accurate measurement that can be drawn.

Plans

A plan may be drawn to show an area of streets or the rooms in a building.

> **KEY POINT**
>
> A grid reference gives the horizontal and vertical readings.

Examples

What are the grid references of the doctor's, dentist's, chemist, station, school, village pond and park?

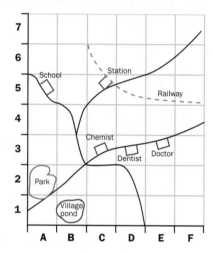

Read the grid by giving a letter and a number.

Doctor's E3, Dentist's D3, Chemist C3, Station C5, School A5, Village pond B1, Park A1/A2

Scale drawing

Any length can be drawn to scale to enable a diagram to fit on a page. Divide each actual measurement by the scale to find the length to be drawn.

> Make sure you quote the scale.

First put the given measurements on a rough sketch. If you are given a scale use it. If not, choose a scale convenient to use, which allows your drawing to fit on a page. A scale that produces too small a drawing will result in inaccuracies.

Examples

Use a scale of 1 : 20 to draw lines representing the following distances:
(a) 28cm **(b)** 1.9m

> Draw to 1 d.p.

(a) 28cm ÷ 20 = 1.4cm ← Divide by scale

(b) 1.9m = 190cm ← Multiply by 100 to convert to cm
190cm ÷ 20 = 9.5cm

Instrument scales

In our everyday life we need to read the scales on numerous instruments. Many instruments now have a digital read-out, but it is still necessary to know how to read off a dial or meter.

Protractor

The 0° – 180° and 90° lines meet at the point of an angle. Place the protractor so that the base line of the angle is underneath it. The point of the angle should be under the meeting points of the lines on the protractor. There are two scales. Read the scale that has 0° on your angle base line.

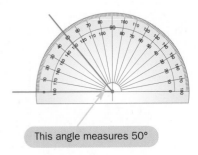

This angle measures 50°

Other instruments

Read the scales on the following instruments:

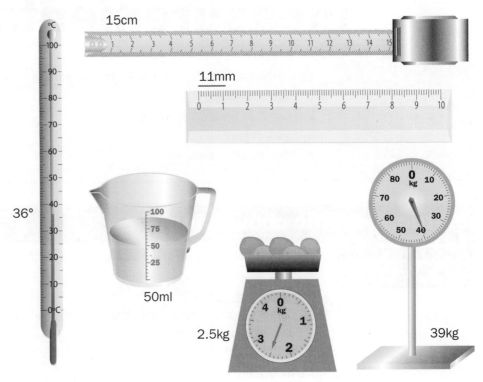

Accuracy

It is important to realise that scales are often inaccurate. Reading the scale on a measuring tool has to be taken to be within certain limits. It is usual to give a length or an angle to 1 decimal place as it is impossible to read more decimal places.

Digital read-outs give more accurate measurements.

PROGRESS CHECK

1. This is a map of the island of Gyrmic. Mark on it:
   (a) Captain's house (G4)
   (b) Lighthouse (A1)
   (c) Smugglers' Inn (D5)
   (d) Farm (F2)

2. If a map scale is 1 : 200 000, calculate the following…
   as map distances
   (a) 8.4km   (b) 125km
   as actual distances
   (c) 4.5cm   (d) 0.54cm

2. (a) 4.2cm (b) 62.5cm
   (c) 9km (d) 1.08km

4.10 Converting measurements

LEARNING SUMMARY	**After studying this section, you should be able to understand:** • metric → metric conversion • metric ↔ imperial conversion • units of time • compound measures

Metric → metric conversion

Unit 1	✗
Unit 2	✗
Unit 3	✓

Measurements are given in the **metric system**. For example, mm, cm, g, l.

KEY POINT

Converting one metric unit to another metric unit involves multiplying or dividing by a power of 10.

You must learn conversion facts such as:

- 10mm = 1cm
- 100cm = 1m
- 1000m = 1km
- 1000mg = 1g
- 1000g = 1kg
- 1000kg = 1 tonne
- 1000ml = 1 litre
- 100cl = 1 litre
- 1000cm^3 = 1 litre

Remember that prefix kilo- and milli- mean 1000 and centi- means 100.

Examples

Change each unit to the one given in brackets.

(a) 0.628kg (g)

$$0.628\text{kg} = 0.628 \times 1000\text{g} \qquad \boxed{1\text{kg} = 1000\text{g}}$$
$$= 628\text{g}$$

(b) 35000cm^2 (m^2)

$$35000\text{cm}^2 = 35000 \div 10000\text{m}^2 \qquad \boxed{1\text{m}^2 = 100\text{cm} \times 100\text{cm}}$$
$$= 3.5\text{m}^2$$

> Multiply if the answer number is going to be larger. Divide if the answer number is going to be smaller.
>
> Remember that if 1m = 100cm, then 1m^2 = 100 × 100 = 10 000cm^2 and 1m^3 = 100 × 100 × 100 = 1 000 000cm^3

Metric ↔ imperial conversion

Unit 1	✗
Unit 2	✗
Unit 3	✓

Measurements were previously given in the **imperial system**. Some of these units are still in use. For example, feet (ft), pint (pt), pounds (lbs), miles.

To change between metric and imperial systems you must learn some appropriate facts.

Approximate metric to imperial conversions:

- **Length**
  8km ≈ 5 miles   2.5cm ≈ 1 inch   30cm ≈ 1 foot   1m ≈ 1 yard (yd)

> It is also useful to know that:
> 1lb = 16 ounces (oz);
> 1 yard (yd) = 3 feet (ft);
> 1 foot (ft) = 12 inches (ins)

- **Area**
  1 hectare (ha) ≈ 2.5 acres ← 1 acre = 4840 square yards
  1 hectare = 10 000m²

- **Volume (capacity)**
  1 litre (l) ≈ 1.75 pints   4.5l ≈ 1 gallon

- **Mass (weight)**
  1kg ≈ 2.2lbs   1 tonne ≈ 1 ton ← Note the different spellings
  1oz ≈ 28g

  Metric   Imperial

Examples

Convert the following to the unit given in brackets.

(a) 3.5lbs (kg)

$$3.5\text{lbs} \approx 3.5 \div 2.2$$ ← 1kg ≈ 2.2lbs

$$\approx 1.6\text{kg}$$

(b) 53km (miles)

$$53\text{km} \approx 53 \times \frac{5}{8}\text{ miles}$$ ← 1km ≈ $\frac{5}{8}$ miles

$$\approx 33\text{ miles}$$ ← Actual answer = 33.125, but this is an appropriate degree of accuracy

> Think about whether the answer is going to be larger or smaller.

Units of time

Unit 1	✗
Unit 2	✗
Unit 3	✓

Time is measured in two different systems based on the 12 hour and 24 hour clocks.

> **KEY POINT**
>
> The **12 hour clock** registers time in two periods of 12 hours a.m. and p.m.
> The **24 hour clock** is a continuous time period of 24 hours.

12 hour clock

> **KEY POINT**
>
> Time period from midnight to noon is a.m.
> Time period from noon to midnight is p.m.

Time given in the 12 hour clock system must be followed by a.m. or p.m. to show whether it is before noon or after noon. For example, 6 a.m. is in the morning and 6 p.m. is in the evening.

24 hour clock

12 hours are added to the morning time to give the afternoon time.

KEY POINT

The 24 hour clock covers the whole 24 hour period. Time is always given with four digits, for example 0600 is 6 o'clock in the morning and 1800 is 6 o'clock in the evening.

Digital clocks give midnight as 0000 or 2400.

You may need to convert times to the other time system, for example:

- 0700 → 7 a.m.
- 7 p.m. → 1900 ← Add 12 + 7 = 19
- 1625 → 4.25 p.m. ← Subtract 16 − 12 = 4

Facts about time

It is important that you learn the following facts:

- 60 seconds (secs) = 1 minute (min)
- 60mins = 1 hour (hr)
- 24hrs = 1 day
- 7 days = 1 week

- 52 weeks = 1 year
- 365 days = 1 year (except in a leap year which has 366 days. A leap year occurs every 4th year.)

Try learning the rhyme '30 days hath September, April, June and November...'

Months have different number of days, usually 30 or 31. Check the calendar for these. February has 28 days in a regular year and 29 days in a leap year.

Example

How long is a TV programme starting at 7.05 p.m. and ending at 8.10 p.m?

7.05 p.m. → 8 p.m = 55mins   60mins = 1hr

7.05 p.m. → 8.10 p.m = 55mins + 10mins = 65mins or 1hr 5mins

Fewer mistakes occur when you use this method.

Do not subtract in the usual way. Remember that time is based on the number 60 not 10.

Compound measures

Unit 1	✗
Unit 2	✗
Unit 3	✓

KEY POINT

Compound measures use more than one unit. Examples are speed, density and rate of flow.

Speed

KEY POINT

Speed = Distance ÷ Time

This formula triangle will help with calculations involving speed.

Speed = Distance ÷ Time
Time = Distance ÷ Speed
Distance = Speed × Time

Speed can be measured in km/hr (kilometres per hour), mph (miles per hour) or m/s (metres per second). Speed gives the distance travelled in one unit of time.

Example

What is the speed of a car taking $3\frac{1}{2}$ hours to drive 200 miles?

$$\text{Speed} = \frac{\text{Distance}}{\text{Time}} = \frac{200}{3.5} \longleftarrow \boxed{\text{Time in hours}}$$

$$= 57\text{mph (to nearest whole number)} \longleftarrow \boxed{\text{Miles per hour}}$$

Average speed

KEY POINT

Average speed over a journey is found by the formula:

$$\text{Average speed} = \frac{\text{Total distance travelled}}{\text{Total time taken}}$$

Example

A train travels 65 miles stopping 5 minutes at each of the 7 stations. It takes 1hr 20mins for the total journey. What is its average speed when travelling?

Time taken for journey = 1hr 20mins − stopping time

$$= 1\text{hr } 20\text{mins} - 35\text{mins} = 45\text{mins}$$

$$\text{Average speed} = \frac{\text{Total distance travelled}}{\text{Total time taken}}$$

$$= \frac{65 \text{ miles}}{45\text{mins}}$$

$$= \frac{65}{0.75} \longleftarrow \boxed{\text{Convert to hours}}$$

$$= 87\text{mph}$$

Density

This formula triangle will help with calculations involving density.

Density = Mass ÷ Volume
Volume = Mass ÷ Density
Mass = Density × Volume

KEY POINT

$$\text{Density} = \frac{\text{Mass}}{\text{Volume}}$$

Density can be measured in kg/m^3 (kilograms per cubic metre)
or g/cm^3 (grams per cubic centimetre).

Calculations involving density can be found on higher level papers.

Example

Find the density of a block of stone weighing 850g with a volume of 92cm^3.

$$\text{Density} = \frac{\text{Mass}}{\text{Volume}}$$

$$= \frac{850}{92}$$

$$= 9.24\text{g/cm}^3 \text{ (3 s.f.)}$$

Other compound measures

Always make sure the working units will give you the required compound units.

KEY POINT

Rate of flow measures the amount of fluid that flows in a given time.
Miles per gallon (mpg) gives the **fuel consumption** over a given distance.

Example

What is the fuel consumption in mpg of a car travelling 200 miles and using 22 litres of fuel?

Fuel = 22l = 22 ÷ 4.5 gallons ⟵ $4.5l \approx 1$ gallon
        = 4.888... gallons

These two stages can be calculated together.

Fuel consumption = 200 ÷ 4.888 = 40.9mpg

PROGRESS CHECK

1. Convert these measurements to the unit given in brackets.
   (a) $42\,500cm^2$ (m^2) (b) 30 000g (kg)
   (c) $450mm^3$ (cm^3) (d) 3.55l (ml) (e) 43.4m (km)

2. This is a recipe for brandy snaps, with quantities given in imperial measures. Rewrite the recipe in metric units. Do all the measures need to be changed?

4ozs butter	3ozs caster sugar
4ozs golden syrup	$3\frac{1}{2}$ozs plain flour
1 tsp ground ginger	1 tsp grated lemon rind

3. This schedule gives TV programme times for an evening.

Time	Programme	Time	Programme
6.35	Local and national news	8.45	Music from the Decade
7.15	Sport catch-up	9.45	Doctor What?
7.40	Move! Move! Move!	11.00	Local and national news
8.10	Celebrity Chase	12.05	World news roundup

   (a) In which clock system are the times given? Is there anything missing from the times?
   (b) How long is Sport catch-up?
   (c) How long are you watching TV for, if you watch Doctor What? followed by the news?
   (d) Convert all the times to the other clock system.

4. Calculate in given units:
   (a) Speed to travel 56 miles in 190mins (mph to 3 s.f)
   (b) Time taken to travel 240km at an average speed of 42mph (hrs to nearest min)
   (c) Density of a piece of rock of mass 2.3kg and volume $80cm^3$ $(g/cm^3$ to 3 s.f)

4.(a) 17.7mph (b) 3hrs 34mins (c) $28.8g/cm^3$
(d) 1835, 1915, 1940, 2010, 2045, 2145, 2300, 0005
3. (a) 12 hour clock; should have p.m. except for 12.05a.m. (b) 25mins (c) 2hrs 20mins
2. 112g butter, 84g caster sugar, 112g golden syrup, 98g plain flour, 1 tsp ground ginger, 1 tsp grated lemon rind; no
1. (a) $4.25m^2$ (b) 30kg (c) $0.45cm^3$ (d) 3550ml (e) 0.0434km

4.11 Estimating

After studying this section, you should be able to understand:

- estimating lines and angles
- estimating area and volume
- estimating weight

Estimating lines and angles

Unit 1 ✗
Unit 2 ✗
Unit 3 ✓

Sometimes it is necessary to make a sensible estimate of a range of measures in real-life situations.

Length

> **Example**
>
> Estimate the height of the bus.
>
> The average estimated height of a man is just under 2 metres.
>
> Judge how many times the picture of the man can fit into the height of the bus and multiply by 2.
>
> It seems to be approximately 2.5 times, so the height of the bus is approximately 5 metres.

Angles

> **Examples**
>
> Estimate the size of the following angles.
>
> **(a)**   **(b)**   **(c)**

Judge where 90° would be with each angle.

> **(a)** This is a reflex angle. The remaining part of the revolution looks as if it is just less than a right angle ∴ it is approximately 275°.
> **(b)** This obtuse angle looks as if it is about 20° more than a right angle ∴ it is approximately 110°.
> **(c)** This acute angle is less than half a right angle ∴ it is approximately 40°.

Estimating area and volume

Unit 1	✗
Unit 2	✗
Unit 3	✓

Estimating an area or volume involves estimating the dimensions first or counting squares or cubes in the shape on a 1cm square grid.

Area

> See pages 173–176 for how to calculate area

Examples

1. Estimate the shaded area of this frame.

   Taking a 'thumb' length, the outside rectangle measures roughly 5cm by 2.5cm. The border seems to be approximately 0.5cm wide.

   > Judge a length by measuring with the top joint of your thumb. This is approximately 2.5cm.

   Shaded area $\approx (5 \times 2.5) - (4 \times 1.5)$ ← Subtract (2×0.5)cm from each dimension
   $= 12.5 - 6 = 6.5\text{cm}^2$

2. Estimate the area of this shape drawn on a 1cm square grid.

   Count all fully included 1cm squares (●) = 74
   Count all squares > one half   = 23
   Ignore all squares < one half
   Total number of squares   = 97
   Estimated area of shape   = 97cm^2

Volume

> See pages 177–180 for how to calculate volume

Examples

1. The side of the square cross-section is 6.5m. Estimate the length and thus the volume of this cuboid.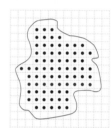

   The length looks approximately double the given side so is approximately 13m.

   Volume $\approx 6.5 \times 6.5 \times 13 = 549.25\text{m}^3$
   It is sensible to give the answer as 550m^3.

2. Estimate the volume of this 3D shape made up of 1cm^3 cubes.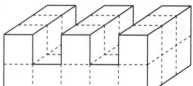

   You need to visualise the cubes you cannot see.

   You can see 8 cubes at the front of the shape. You can see 3 rows of cubes at the side of the shape.

   Total number of cubes = $8 \times 3 = 24$
   Estimated volume of shape = 24cm^3

Estimating weight

Unit 1	✗
Unit 2	✗
Unit 3	✓

Weight often needs to be estimated in everyday situations. For example, the weight of loose fruit and vegetables is gauged if there are no scales at the supermarket.

Example

How much does a loaf of bread weigh?

80g, 800g, 8kg or 80kg

The answer has to be sensible. You should realise that 8kg and 80kg are far too heavy. If you compare the loaf to a bag of sugar, which weighs 1kg or 1000g, then the loaf probably weighs 800g.

PROGRESS CHECK

🖩 Without using a calculator

1 Estimate the following measures and give the appropriate units:
   (a) The length of a bench that can seat three people
   (b) The height of a garage door
   (c) The capacity of a wine glass
   (d) The area of a tennis court
   (e) The mass of a small car.

2 Estimate the sizes of these angles.
   (a)　　　**(b)**　　　**(c)**　　　**(d)**

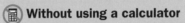

3 Estimate the volume of this shape drawn with 1cm cubes.

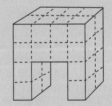

1. Accept any sensible answer: (a) 1.5m (b) 2m (c) 150ml (d) 200m² (e) 1t
2. (a) 35° (b) 110° (c) 315° (d) 210°　3. 24cm³

4.12 Bearings

LEARNING SUMMARY	After studying this section, you should be able to understand:
	<ul><li>compass points</li><li>three-figure bearings</li><li>bearings diagrams</li></ul>

Compass points

Unit 1 ✗
Unit 2 ✗
Unit 3 ✓

KEY POINT

The four main **compass points** are North, South, East and West. The initial letters are usually used.

There is a right angle between:

- North and East
- East and South
- South and West
- West and North

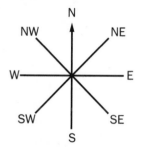

NE, SE, SW and NW points bisect each right angle. These angles are always measured clockwise from North. East is at 90°, South is at 180°, West is at 270°.

Example

Measuring clockwise from North…

(a) what is the angle between N and SE?

Angle = 3 × 45° = 135°

(b) what is the angle between NW and S?

Angle = 45° + 180° = 225°

Three-figure bearings

Unit 1   ✗
Unit 2   ✗
Unit 3   ✓

KEY POINT

Bearings are used to describe directions. Bearings are measured using angles in a clockwise direction from the North line.

The direction of point B from A is given by the angle measured clockwise from North at point A and written as a **three-figure** angle.

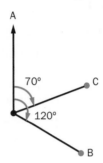

The bearing of B from A = 120°

The bearing of C from A = 070° ←   Use zero to make three figures

---

Reverse bearing is also known as the reciprocal or back bearing.

KEY POINT

If the bearing is given for a journey from X to Y, the **reverse bearing** gives the angle for the return journey (Y to X).

Example

Find the bearing from X to Y in each drawing and then find the bearing for the return journeys from Y to X.

(a)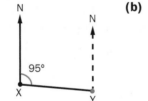
    (b)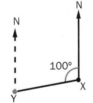

Diagrams not drawn to scale

It is necessary to draw North lines at Y. These are obviously parallel to the North lines at X. The bearing at Y is the clockwise angle from the North line to line YX.

(a) Bearing from X to Y = 095°

$$\angle NYX = 180° - 95° = 85°$$
$$\text{Reverse bearing} = 360° - 85° = 275°$$
$$(\text{or} = 180° + 95° = 275°)$$

Interior angles are supplementary – add up to 180°

Alternate angles are equal

Angles on a straight line add up to 180°

(b) Bearing from X to Y = 360° − 100° = 260°

$$\text{Reverse bearing} = 180° - 100° = 080°$$

Interior angles are supplementary – add up to 180°

Bearings diagrams

Unit 1   ✗
Unit 2   ✗
Unit 3   ✓

Never assume diagrams are accurate unless told so.

Given diagrams

You may be given a diagram of a journey and asked to calculate bearings or distances. Trigonometry or Pythagoras' theorem are often used.

Example

E and H are two small coastal towns. B is a village nearby. A lighthouse (L) is situated on the direct route from H to B, so that a perpendicular line joins it to E.

(a) Calculate the bearing of H from E, B from H and B from E.
(b) Calculate the distance from H to B.

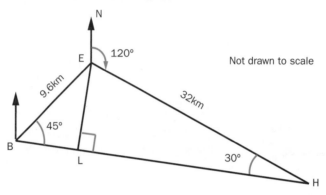

Not drawn to scale

(a) Bearing of H from E = 120°
Bearing of B from H = 360° − 30° − 60° = 270°
Bearing of B from E = 120° + 105° = 225°

> Interior angles are supplementary

> Angle sum of △ EHB

(b) Draw in the line LE. △ EHL and △ ELB are both right-angled.
Use trigonometric ratios to find HL and LB, thus finding HB.

In EHL, $\frac{LH}{32} = \cos 30°$

$LH = 32 \times \cos 30° = 27.7$km (3 s.f.)

In ELB, $\frac{LB}{9.6} = \cos 45°$

$LB = 9.6 \times \cos 45° = 6.79$km (3 s.f.)

∴ Distance HB = 27.7 + 6.79 = 34.49km = 34.5km (3 s.f.)

Drawing scale diagrams

Drawing scale diagrams involves drawing lengths and angles to scale, as well as measuring other lengths and converting them back to actual distances.

Example

A ship sails 25km from port A on a bearing of 070° to port C. It then sails 30km due east to port B, before returning directly to port A. Use a scale drawing to find the distance and bearing of the return journey.

It is useful to draw a rough sketch first.

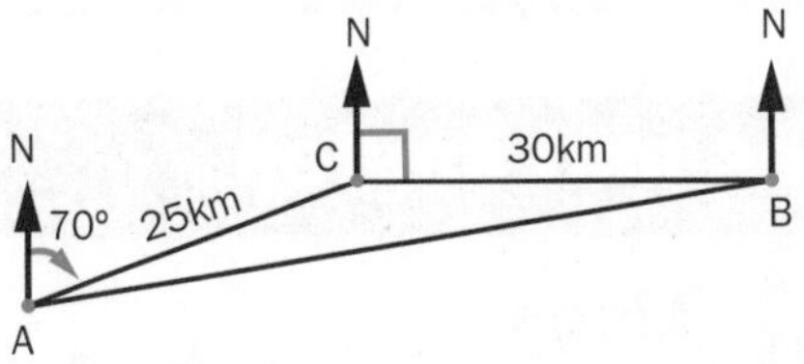

Choose a scale to fit the diagram on the page, e.g. scale 1cm : 10km

Place port A and draw in a North line. Measure 70° from North line clockwise. Measure 2.5cm (25km) and mark port C.

At port C, draw another North line. Measure 90° from North line clockwise. Measure 3cm (30km) and mark port B.

N to E is a right angle

Join B to A and measure the distance with a ruler.

Actual distance = 5.4cm × 10km = 54km

Use a protractor to measure ∠ CBA = 9°

Bearing of A from B = 360° – 90° – 9° = 261°
(or = 180° + 81° = 261°)

PROGRESS CHECK

Without using a calculator

1. What is the bearing of P from R in each of these diagrams?

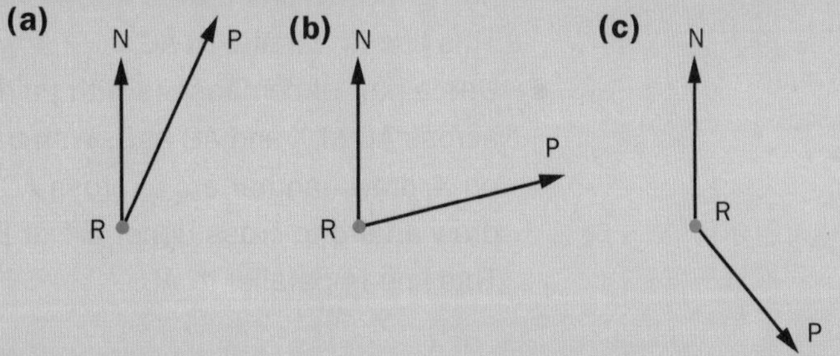

2. A ferry sails 25km from port A on a bearing of 085° and then 30km due East to port B. It then sails directly back to A. Use a scale drawing to find out how far the return journey is and on what bearing does the ferry need to sail to return to A?

1. (a) 025° (b) 077° (c) 140°

2.

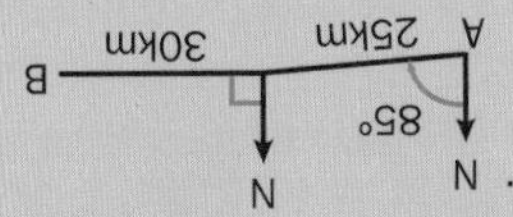

Not drawn to scale

Return journey = 55km, bearing = 267°

4.13 Constructions and loci

After studying this section, you should be able to understand:

- drawing lines and angles
- drawing triangles
- drawing quadrilaterals and inscribed polygons
- constructing loci

Drawing lines and angles

Unit 1   *X*
Unit 2   *X*
Unit 3   ✓

Lines

> Always use a sharp pencil for drawing accurate constructions. Never draw with pen in case you make a mistake.

Example

(a) Draw a line AB measuring 2.5cm.

(b) At A draw a line AC at an angle of 65°.

(c) Draw a line parallel to AC to cut AB at D.

(a) Use a ruler to draw a line and measure a length of 2.5cm. Mark this length AB.

(b) Use a protractor to measure an angle of 65° at A. Draw line AC.

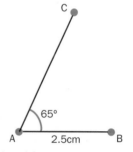

(c) There are three ways to draw a line parallel to AC.

- Mark a point D on AB and measure an angle of 65° at D. This line will be parallel to AC because of the corresponding angles.

- Place a set square so that its hypotenuse is against AC. Place a straight edge along another side. Slide the set square along the straight edge and draw a line along the hypotenuse to cut AB at D. This line is parallel to AC.

- Use a pair of compasses with point on A and draw an arc to cut across AC at X and AB at D. With the same compass width and point on X, draw another arc to cross AC at Y and then with point on D draw an arc to cross upper arc at E. Draw a line through D and E. This line is parallel to AC.

> Always leave the arcs on your drawing. They show your method of construction.

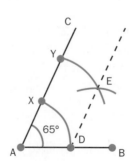

Angles

Some angles can be constructed using only a ruler and a pair of compasses.

- **60°**

  1. Draw line and mark point A at one end.
  2. Use a pair of compasses to draw arc cutting line at B.
  3. With same compass width and point on B, draw a second arc to cross the first arc at C.
  4. Join A to C.

  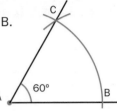

  > If you are given length AB, use this as the compass width. Otherwise use any length.

- **30°**

  1. First draw an angle of 60° (as above).
  2. With same compass width and point first on B and then C, draw arcs to cross at X.
  3. Join A to X. This is the **bisector** of ∠ BAC.

  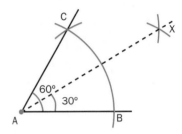

- **90°**

  1. Draw line and mark point A at one end.
  2. Draw a circle, centre O, to pass through A and cut line at B.
  3. Draw line from B, through O, to circumference at C.
  4. BC is the diameter of the circle, centre O. Join A to C. ∠ BAC = 90° (Angle in semicircle)

  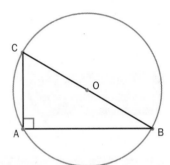

- **45°**

  First draw an angle of 90° as above and then bisect to form 45°

  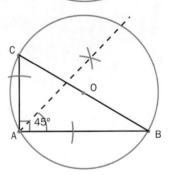

- **Drawing a perpendicular from point P to a line**

  1. With compass point on P, draw arcs to cut line at Q and R.
  2. With same compass width and point on Q and then R, draw arcs to cross below line.
  3. Join crossed arcs to P to form perpendicular.

  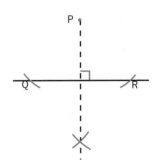

Drawing triangles

Unit 1	X
Unit 2	X
Unit 3	✓

Triangles can be drawn using a ruler, protractor and a pair of compasses.

- **When three sides are given**
  1. Draw line XY and measure to given length.
  2. With compass width equal to XZ and point on X, draw an arc.
  3. With compass width equal to YZ and point on Y, draw a second arc.

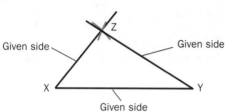

- **When two sides and an angle are given**
  1. Draw line XY and measure to given length.
  2. Use a protractor to measure and draw angle Y.
  3. Measure length YZ and mark Z.
  4. Join XZ.

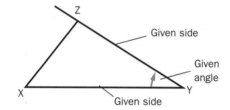

- **When two angles and a side are given**
  1. Draw line XY and measure to given length.
  2. Use a protractor to measure and draw given angles at X and Y.
  3. Z is the point where these lines meet.

> This only works if the given side lies between the given angles.

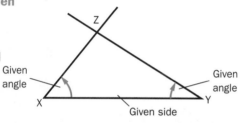

Drawing quadrilaterals and inscribed polygons

Unit 1	X
Unit 2	X
Unit 3	✓

Drawing quadrilaterals

Drawing a quadrilateral is just an extension of drawing triangles.

> **Example**
>
> Construct a quadrilateral ABCD with AB = 6.5cm, AC = 5cm, BD = 5.8cm
> ∠ BDC = 100°, ∠ ABD = 72°,
> Measure CD and ∠ BAC
>
> > Draw a rough sketch first.
>
>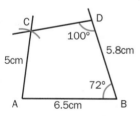
>
> - Draw line AB to given length.
> - Measure and draw angle 72° at B.
> - Measure length BD and mark D.
> - Measure and draw angle 100° at D.
> - With a pair of compasses, draw an arc of 5cm, centre A, crossing line from D. Mark this point C. Join AC.
> - Measure CD = 4cm, ∠ BAC = 82°
>
> Not drawn to scale

Inscribed polygons

> **KEY POINT**
>
> An **inscribed polygon** is a polygon drawn in a circle with all vertices on the circumference.

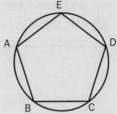

Follow these steps to draw an **inscribed hexagon**:

1. Draw a circle.
2. Mark a point A on the circumference.
3. Keeping compass width the same as the radius and point on A, draw a small arc to cut the circumference.
4. Repeat, moving the compass point to the intersection of the arc and the circumference around the circle.
5. Join each pair of points with a chord so that a hexagon is formed.

> You should find that each chord (side of the hexagon) equals the radius.

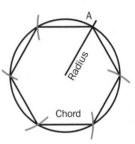

Constructing loci

Unit 1   ✗
Unit 2   ✗
Unit 3   ✓

> **KEY POINT**
>
> A **locus** is the path of a point that moves according to a given rule. Loci is the plural of locus.

- The locus of a point, moving at a fixed distance r from a fixed point C is a circle. Draw circle, radius r, centre, C.

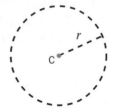

- The locus of a point, moving at a constant distance from a line through two fixed points A and B, is a pair of straight lines parallel to AB and at a distance d from AB.
  1. Draw line AB.
  2. Measure distance d above and below A and B.
  3. Join points to form two parallel lines.

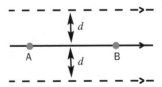

- The locus of a point, equidistant from two fixed points A and B, is the **perpendicular bisector** of AB.

  ① Draw line AB.
  ② Using compass width over half the length of AB and centres A and B, draw arcs to cross above and below AB.
  ③ Join these cross points to form the perpendicular bisector cutting AB in half at right angles.

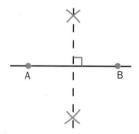

- The locus of a point equidistant from two fixed lines, is the bisector of the angle between the lines.

  ① Draw line XZ.
  ② Measure ∠ YXZ with a protractor.
  ③ With compass point on X, draw arcs to cut XY and XZ.
  ④ Keeping same compass width and compass point on the points of intersection of the arcs and lines, draw arcs to cross between the lines.
  ⑤ Join crossed arcs to X to form angle bisector.

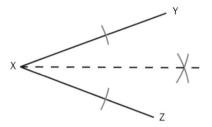

PROGRESS CHECK

📱 **Without using a calculator**

① Use only ruler and a pair of compasses for this question.
   (a) Construct triangle CDE with CD = 8cm, ∠ C = 45°, ∠ D = 60°.
   (b) Bisect ∠ CED. Mark point X at intersection with CD.
   (c) Measure CX and ∠ CEX to the nearest degree.
   (d) How can you check that you have the correct value for ∠ CEX? Show your working.

② A market gardener is pestered by birds eating his fruit berries. A straight path of 8km (PR) runs through the middle of his fruit bushes. He decides to place scarecrows, at a variable point S, to frighten the birds away. S is always a distance of 5km from the midpoint (M) of PR and 4km from PR. By constructing the loci of S satisfying these conditions, find the positions that the market gardener can place his scarecrows.

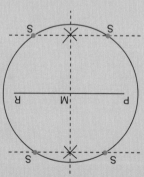

Your diagram should be drawn to scale:
Distance SM = 5km
Distance PM = 4km
Distance M to arcs = 4km

2.

1. (c) CX = 4.4cm, ∠CEX = 38° (d) ∠CEX = $\frac{1}{2}$(180° − 45° − 60°) = 37.5 (angle sum of ∆ = 180°)
= 38° to the nearest degree

4.14 Area and perimeter

	After studying this section, you should be able to understand:
LEARNING SUMMARY	<ul><li>perimeter</li><li>area and perimeter of 2D shapes</li><li>area and perimeter of circles</li><li>area and perimeter of compound shapes</li></ul>

Perimeter

Unit 1	✗
Unit 2	✗
Unit 3	✓

> **KEY POINT**
>
> The **perimeter** of a shape is the distance all around the edge.

For example:

Remember to count all the sides.

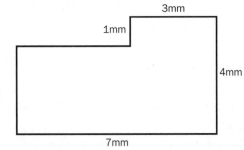

Perimeter = (7 + 4 + 3 + 1 + 4 + 3)mm
= 22mm

Area and perimeter of 2D shapes

Unit 1	✗
Unit 2	✗
Unit 3	✓

Area is always measured in squared units.

Name	Shape	Perimeter	Area
Square		$4a$	a^2
Rectangle		$2(b + h)$	bh
Parallelogram		$2(a + b)$ a = slant height	bh h = perpendicular height
Trapezium		$a + b + c + d$	$\frac{1}{2}(a + b)h$
Triangle		$a + b + c$	$\frac{1}{2}bh$ (half a parallelogram)

Examples

Calculate the areas of these shapes.

(a)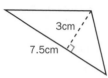

(b)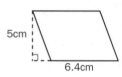

(c)

Diagrams not drawn to scale

(a) Area = $\frac{1}{2}$ × 7.5 × 3 = 11.25cm²

(b) Area = 6.4 × 5 = 32cm²

(c) Area = $\frac{1}{2}$(5 + 7) × 4.2 = 25.2cm²

Area and perimeter of circles

Unit 1 ✗
Unit 2 ✗
Unit 3 ✓

KEY POINT

The perimeter of a circle is called the circumference (C). The formula for the perimeter of a circle is:

$C = 2\pi r$ or $C = \pi d$ ← Diameter (d) = 2 × radius (r)

The formula for the area of a circle (A) is:

$A = \pi r^2$

(Use π = 3.142 or π key on the calculator. You may sometimes need to use $\pi = \frac{22}{7}$ or $\pi \approx 3$)

> Check if the radius or diameter is given in the question. Radius is needed to calculate area.

Example

Find the circumference and area of a circle, radius = 3.4cm.

$C = 2\pi r$
$\quad = 2\pi(3.4)$
$\quad = 6.8\pi$
$\quad = 21.4$cm   (3 s.f.)
$A = \pi r^2$
$\quad = \pi(3.4)^2$
$\quad = 36.3$cm²   (3 s.f.)

> You may be asked to find the length of an arc or the area of a sector on higher level papers.

Length of an arc and area of a sector

An arc is part of the circumference of a circle. It subtends an angle at the centre of a circle. A sector is a section of a circle between two radii and an arc.

KEY POINT

If the angle is θ and the radius is r

Length of arc = $\frac{\theta}{360°} \times 2\pi r$

Area of sector = $\frac{\theta}{360°} \times \pi r^2$

> $= \frac{\theta}{360°}$ gives the fraction the sector is of the circle.

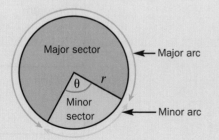

Example

(a) Find the length of the minor arc of a circle, diameter = 11cm, subtending an angle of 55° and (b) the area of its minor sector.

(a) Length of arc $= \dfrac{55}{360} \times \pi \times 11$ ← $d = 11\text{cm}$

$= 5.28\text{cm}$

(b) Area of sector $= \dfrac{55}{360} \times \pi \times (5.5)^2$ ← $r = 11 \div 2\text{cm}$

$= 14.5\text{cm}^2$

> You may be asked to find the area of a segment on higher level papers.

Area of a segment

A segment is the area between a chord and the circumference.

KEY POINT

Area of minor segment = area of minor sector − △ AOB
Area of major segment = area of major sector + △ AOB

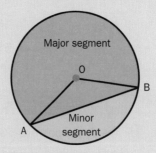

Example

Calculate the area of the major segment of this circle:

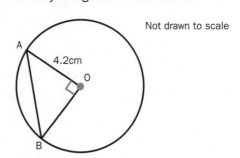

Not drawn to scale

Area of major sector $= \dfrac{270}{360} \times \pi \times (4.2)^2$ ← $360° - 90° = 270°$

$= 41.56\text{cm}^2$

Area of △ AOB $= \dfrac{1}{2} \times 4.2 \times 4.2$ ← $\frac{1}{2}bh$

$= 8.82\text{cm}^2$

Area of major segment $= 41.56 + 8.82$

$= 50.38$

$= 50.4\text{cm}^2$ (1 d.p.)

Area and perimeter of compound shapes

Unit 1	✗
Unit 2	✗
Unit 3	✓

You may be asked to find the area and perimeter of a figure made up of different shapes.

> Area and perimeter of compound shapes can be found on higher level papers.

Example

Not drawn to scale

A window is made up of glass and thin metal strips.
What area of glass and length of metal strip is required?

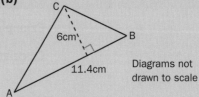

50cm

80cm

> Area of semicircle = $\frac{1}{2}$ area circle

Area of glass = $(50 \times 80) + \frac{1}{2}(\pi(40)^2)$

> $\frac{1}{2}$ diameter = radius

$= 4000 + 2513 = 6513\text{cm}^2$

Length of metal strip = $(80 \times 2) + (50 \times 3) + (2 \times 40) + \frac{1}{2}\pi \times 80$

> Circumference of semicircle = $\frac{1}{2}$ circumference of circle

$= 160 + 150 + 80 + 126$

$= 516\text{cm}$

PROGRESS CHECK

1. These shapes are plans for flower beds in a park. Find the area of each shape and the perimeters of **(a)** and **(d)**

(a)

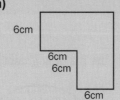

6cm
6cm
6cm
6cm

(b)

C
6cm
B
11.4cm
A

Diagrams not drawn to scale

(c)

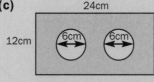

24cm
12cm
6cm 6cm

(d)

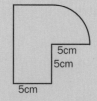

5cm
5cm
5cm

2. **(a)** Calculate the length of the major arc of a circle, radius 3.4cm, subtending an angle of 120°

   (b) Calculate...

   (i) the area of the minor sector

   (ii) the area of the minor segment formed by a chord joining the ends of this arc.

2.(a) 14.2cm (b) (i) 12.1cm² (ii) 7.1cm²
1. (a) A = 108cm², P = 48cm (b) A = 34.2cm² (c) A = 231.5cm² (d) A = 69.6cm², P = 37.9cm

4.15 Volume and surface area

LEARNING SUMMARY	After studying this section, you should be able to understand:
	• volume and surface area of cubes and cuboids
	• volume and surface area of other 3D shapes
	• volume and surface area of compound solid shapes

Volume and surface area of cubes and cuboids

Unit 1	X
Unit 2	X
Unit 3	✓

See Geometry 4.7 for different types of 3D shapes.

Imagine the 3D shape opened out into its net.

KEY POINT

Volume of a cube (side s) = s^3

> Volume is always measured in cubed units.

Volume of a cuboid (sides l, b, h) = lbh

> length × breadth × height

To find surface area, add areas of all faces.

Surface area of a cube = $6 \times s^2 = 6s^2$ ← 6 faces

Surface area of a cuboid = $2(lb + lh + bh)$ ← 2 of each different face

Examples

(a) Find the volume and surface area of a cuboid l = 6cm, b = 4cm, h = 3cm

Volume = lbh = 6 × 4 × 3 = 72cm³

Surface area = 2((6 × 4) + (6 × 3) + (4 × 3))

= 2(24 + 18 + 12)

= 2 × 54

= 108cm²

(b) Find the side of a cube and its surface area if its volume is 125cm³.

Side = $\sqrt[3]{125}$ = 5cm

Surface area = 6 × 5²

= 150cm²

Volume and surface area of other 3D shapes

Unit 1	X
Unit 2	X
Unit 3	✓

Prisms

A prism takes its name from the shape of its cross-section.

KEY POINT

Volume of a prism = area of its cross-section × length (or height)

Surface area of a prism = sum of area of all faces

● **Triangular prism**

KEY POINT

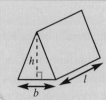

Area of cross-section = $\frac{1}{2}bh$

∴ volume = $\frac{1}{2}bhl$

Surface area = 2 triangles + 3 rectangles

Example

Find the volume and surface area of a triangular prism where $h = 5$cm, $b = 4$cm and $l = 6$cm.

Volume = $\frac{1}{2}(4 \times 5) \times 6 = 60$cm^3

To find the surface area, we need to find the side of the rectangle(s):

Using Pythagoras: $s^2 = 5^2 + 2^2$ ← $\frac{1}{2}$ base of triangle

$= 25 + 4 = 29$

$= \sqrt{29} = 5.39$cm

2 triangles + 2 rectangles + base

∴ surface area = $2(\frac{1}{2} \times 4 \times 5) + 2(5.39 \times 6) + (4 \times 6)$

$= 20 + 64.68 + 24 = 108.68$cm^2 = 109cm^2

Answers have been corrected to 3 s.f. or nearest whole number where appropriate.

● **Cylinder**

A cylinder is a prism with a circle as its cross-section.

KEY POINT

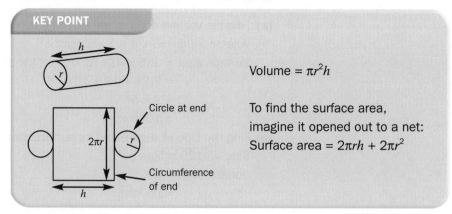

Circle at end

Circumference of end

Volume = $\pi r^2 h$

To find the surface area, imagine it opened out to a net:

Surface area = $2\pi rh + 2\pi r^2$

Example

Find the volume and surface area of a can of tomato soup where $d = 7$cm, $h = 10$cm.

$\frac{1}{2}$ diameter = radius

Volume = $\pi r^2 h = \pi(3.5)^2 \times 10 = 384.8 = 385$cm^3

Surface area = $2\pi(3.5 \times 10) + 2\pi(3.5)^2$

$= 219.91 + 76.97$

$= 296.88$

$= 297$cm^2 ← Give answer to nearest whole number

Pyramids

You may be asked to find the volume and surface area of pyramids, cones, frustum of cones and spheres on higher level papers.

KEY POINT

Volume of a pyramid $= \frac{1}{3} \times$ area of base $\times$ perpendicular height

Surface area of pyramid = sum of area of all faces

Square-based pyramid   **Tetrahedron (4 faces)**

A pyramid usually takes its name from the shape of its base.

Cones

KEY POINT

Volume of a cone $= \frac{1}{3} \times$ area of base $\times$ perpendicular height

$V = \frac{1}{3}\pi r^2 h$ where r is the radius of the base

Curved surface area $= \pi r l$ where l is the slant height

Frustum of cone

KEY POINT

A frustum of a cone is produced when the top of the cone is sliced parallel to the base.

Volume of a frustum

= volume of whole cone − volume of removed cone

$= \frac{1}{3}\pi R^2 H - \frac{1}{3}\pi r^2 h$

Curved surface area of frustum

$=$ curved surface area of the whole cone $-$ curved surface area of removed cone

$= \pi R L - \pi r l$ where l is the slant height

You may need to add the areas of the circles at the top and bottom of the frustum. Read the question carefully.

Spheres

KEY POINT

Volume of sphere $= \frac{4}{3}\pi r^3$ where r is the radius of the sphere

Surface area of sphere $= 4\pi r^2$

Halve the volume of a sphere to find the volume of a hemisphere.

Volume and surface area of compound solid shapes

Unit 1   X
Unit 2   X
Unit 3   ✓

KEY POINT

To find the volume and surface area of compound solid shapes add together all the components required. It may not be every face. Always check that units are consistent.

> Volume and surface area of compound solid shapes can be found on higher level papers.

Example

A baby's toy consists of a cone on top of a hemisphere. Calculate its volume and surface area.

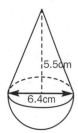

5.5cm

6.4cm

Not drawn to scale

Volume of cone $= \frac{1}{3}\pi r^2 h$

> $\frac{1}{2}$ diameter = radius

$= \frac{1}{3} \times \pi \times 3.2^2 \times 5.5$

$= 58.98\text{cm}^3$

Volume of hemisphere $= \frac{1}{2} \times \frac{4}{3} \times \pi \times 3.2^3$

$= 68.63\text{cm}^3$

Total volume of toy $= 58.98 + 68.63 = 127.6 = 128\text{cm}^3$ (3 s.f.)

Slant height is needed to find surface area. Using Pythagoras' theorem:

$l^2 = 5.5^2 + 3.2^2 = 30.25 + 10.24 = 40.49$

$l = \sqrt{40.49} = 6.36\text{cm}$

Curved surface area of cone $= \pi rl = \pi \times 3.2 \times \sqrt{40.49}$

$= 63.97\text{cm}^2$

> Flat surface of hemisphere is not needed in this calculation.

Curved surface area of hemisphere $= \frac{1}{2}(4\pi r^2) = \frac{1}{2} \times 4\pi \times 3.2^2$

$= 64.34\text{cm}^2$

Total curved surface area of toy $= 63.97 + 64.34 = 128.31 = 128\text{cm}^2$ (3 s.f.)

PROGRESS CHECK

1. A decorative box of sweets is made from a cube, sides of 10cm.
   (a) What is the total capacity of the box?
   (b) What is the area of card needed to make the box?
2. Find the volume and total surface area of a solid rod made from a cylinder of length 15cm and radius 85mm with a hemisphere on each end.
3. A tent is in the form of a square based pyramid with a floor of side 5 metres. The top point (vertex) of the tent is directly over the centre point of the floor. The cubic capacity of the tent is 100m².
   (a) Find the slant edge of the tent (s)
   (b) What is the area of material needed to make the whole tent, including the floor?
4. What is the capacity of a plant pot formed from an inverted cone, diameter 20cm and height 38cm, with its top, diameter 10cm and height 14cm, sliced off? Give your answer to 3 s.f.

1. a) Capacity of box = 1000cm³ b) Area of card = 600cm²   2. volume = 5977cm³; surface area = 1709cm²   3. (a)12.5m (b) 147.5m²   4. capacity = 3612.8 = 3610cm³

4.16 Effect of enlargement

After studying this section, you should be able to understand:

- the effect of enlargement on length, area and volume

Effect of enlargement on length, area and volume

Unit 1 ✗
Unit 2 ✗
Unit 3 ✓

Length, area and volume can be enlarged by multiplying by a **scale factor**.

- **Length**

  Enlarge the length 2cm by scale factor 3.5

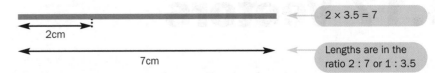

2cm

$2 \times 3.5 = 7$

7cm

Lengths are in the ratio 2 : 7 or 1 : 3.5

- **Area**

  Enlarge a square, of sides 2.5cm, by scale factor 2, i.e. multiply each length by 2. What is the effect on the area?

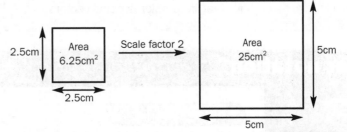

2.5cm — Area 6.25cm² — 2.5cm

Scale factor 2

Area 25cm² — 5cm — 5cm

Scale factor = $\dfrac{\text{enlarged area}}{\text{original area}}$

Area enlarges by scale factor $\dfrac{25}{6.25} = 4 = 2^2$

Areas are in the ratio 2 : 2²

KEY POINT

If the side of a shape enlarges by scale factor a, the area enlarges by scale factor a^2.

Enlargement of area of volume can be found on higher level papers.

- **Volume**

  Enlarge a cube, of sides 2.5cm, by scale factor 2. What is the effect on the volume?

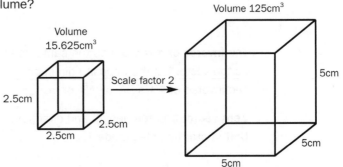

Volume 15.625cm³

2.5cm
2.5cm
2.5cm

Scale factor 2

Volume 125cm³

5cm
5cm
5cm

Scale factor = $\dfrac{\text{enlarged volume}}{\text{original volume}}$

Volume enlarges by scale factor $\dfrac{125}{15.625} = 8 = 2^3$

Volumes are in the ratio 2 : 2³

KEY POINT

If the side of a shape enlarges by scale factor a, the volume enlarges by scale factor a^3.

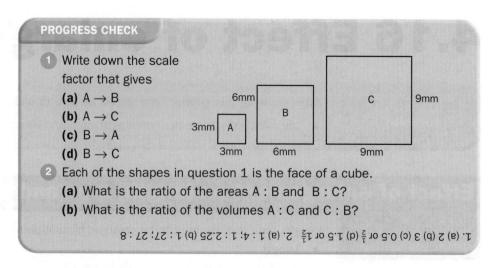

PROGRESS CHECK

1. Write down the scale factor that gives
   (a) A → B
   (b) A → C
   (c) B → A
   (d) B → C

2. Each of the shapes in question 1 is the face of a cube.
   (a) What is the ratio of the areas A : B and B : C?
   (b) What is the ratio of the volumes A : C and C : B?

1. (a) 2 (b) 3 (c) 0.5 or $\frac{2}{3}$ (d) 1.5 or 1$\frac{1}{2}$ 2. (a) 1 : 4 ; 1 : 2.25 (b) 1 : 27 ; 27 : 8

4.17 Vectors

LEARNING SUMMARY	After studying this section, you should be able to understand:
	• vector notation
	• addition and subtraction of vectors
	• real-life problems using vectors

Vector notation

Unit 1	✗
Unit 2	✗
Unit 3	✓

Vectors can be found on higher level papers.

KEY POINT

A **vector** gives magnitude (size) and direction.

When a shape is translated, a column vector such as $\binom{2}{3}$ is used to describe the translation.

Vectors are also written using $\overrightarrow{AB}$ meaning that the vector starts at A and ends at B. They may also be written in the form **a** or a̰

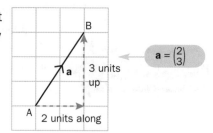

The **inverse of a vector** has the same size as the vector but the opposite direction. The inverse of $\overrightarrow{AB}$ is $\overrightarrow{BA}$ or $-\overrightarrow{AB}$ or -**a**.

Zero vector has zero length and direction.
Unit vector has magnitude 1.

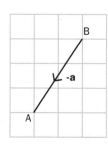

Scalars

KEY POINT

A **scalar** is a quantity that multiplies a vector to give another vector. It has magnitude but not direction.

For example:

$$s = \begin{pmatrix} 2 \\ -2 \end{pmatrix}$$

$$\therefore 2s = 2\begin{pmatrix} 2 \\ -2 \end{pmatrix} = \begin{pmatrix} 4 \\ -4 \end{pmatrix}$$

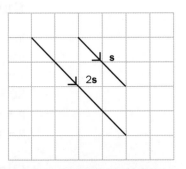

Multiplying the vectors by 2 doubles the length. The direction remains the same, so the vectors are parallel.

Addition and subtraction of vectors

Unit 1   ✗
Unit 2   ✗
Unit 3   ✓

> **KEY POINT**
>
> Addition and subtraction of vectors produces a further vector called the **resultant**.

Addition of vectors

- **Finding the resultant**

    When two vectors are added, the resultant vector is found by adding the horizontal units and then the vertical units:

    $$\begin{pmatrix} a \\ b \end{pmatrix} + \begin{pmatrix} c \\ d \end{pmatrix} = \begin{pmatrix} a + c \\ b + d \end{pmatrix}$$

    > **Example**
    >
    > Find the resultant vector $\vec{CE}$ when $\vec{CD} = \begin{pmatrix} 3 \\ 4 \end{pmatrix}$ and $\vec{DE} = \begin{pmatrix} 2 \\ -1 \end{pmatrix}$
    >
    > $\vec{CE} = \vec{CD} + \vec{DE}$
    >
    > $\quad = \begin{pmatrix} 3 \\ 4 \end{pmatrix} + \begin{pmatrix} 2 \\ -1 \end{pmatrix}$
    >
    > $\quad = \begin{pmatrix} 3 + 2 \\ 4 + -1 \end{pmatrix} = \begin{pmatrix} 5 \\ 3 \end{pmatrix}$

- **Triangle law**

    Adding $\vec{PQ}$ and $\vec{QR}$ gives the resultant $\vec{PR}$.
    These vectors form a triangle.
    This can be written as **p + q = r**

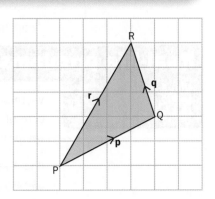

- **Parallelogram law**

    If the triangle above is developed into a parallelogram:
    $\vec{PQ} + \vec{QR} = \vec{PR}$ and $\vec{PS} + \vec{SR} = \vec{PR}$
    So **p + q = r** whichever way round the parallelogram is taken.
    i.e. **p + q = q + p = r**

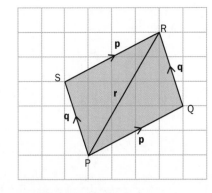

Subtraction of vectors

In order to move from P to R it is necessary to
use the inverse vector.

The inverse of $\vec{QR}$ is $\vec{RQ}$ or $-\vec{QR}$.

$\vec{RQ} = \mathbf{q}$

$\mathbf{p} + -\mathbf{q} = \mathbf{r}$

$\mathbf{p} - \mathbf{q} = \mathbf{r}$

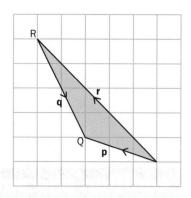

Example

ABCD is a quadrilateral.

M, N and P are midpoints as shown.

$\vec{AB} = \mathbf{a}$, $\vec{CB} = \mathbf{c}$, $\vec{AD} = \mathbf{b}$, $\vec{DC} = \mathbf{d}$

Find **(a)** $\vec{AC}$ **(b)** $\vec{PA}$ **(c)** $\vec{MP}$ **(d)** $\vec{AM}$ **(e)** $\vec{NP}$

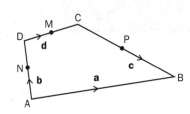

(a) $\vec{AC} = \vec{AD} + \vec{DC} = \mathbf{b} + \mathbf{d}$

    or $\vec{AC} = \vec{AB} + \vec{BC} = \mathbf{a} - \mathbf{c}$

(b) $\vec{PA} = \vec{PB} + \vec{BA} = \frac{1}{2}\vec{CB} + (-\vec{AB}) = \frac{1}{2}\mathbf{c} - \mathbf{a}$

> P is midpoint of $\vec{CB}$, so is half CB   Inverse vector

(c) $\vec{MP} = \frac{1}{2}\vec{DC} + \frac{1}{2}\vec{CB} = \frac{1}{2}\mathbf{d} + \frac{1}{2}\mathbf{c} = \frac{1}{2}(\mathbf{d} + \mathbf{c})$ Common factor $\frac{1}{2}$

(d) $\vec{AM} = \vec{AD} + \vec{DM} = \mathbf{b} + \frac{1}{2}\mathbf{d}$

(e) $\vec{NP} = \vec{ND} + \vec{DC} + \vec{CP} = \frac{1}{2}\mathbf{b} + \mathbf{d} + \frac{1}{2}\mathbf{c}$

    or $\vec{NP} = \vec{NA} + \vec{AB} + \vec{BP} = (-\frac{1}{2}\mathbf{d}) + \mathbf{a} + (-\frac{1}{2}\mathbf{c}) = \frac{-\mathbf{d}}{2} + \mathbf{a} - \frac{\mathbf{c}}{2} = \mathbf{a} - \frac{1}{2}(\mathbf{c} + \mathbf{d})$

Real-life problems using vectors

Unit 1	✗
Unit 2	✗
Unit 3	✓

Vectors are used to represent real-life problems involving forces such as river
current, wind speed, etc. Swimming or sailing across a river are common
vector problems.

It is always a good idea to adjust the given information into known vectors and
use a vector triangle or parallelogram.

Examples

Jasmine swims across a river at 2.5m/s. The current is flowing at 2m/s.

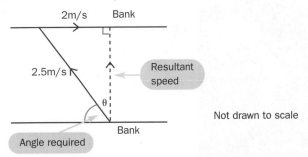

Not drawn to scale

(a) At what angle to the bank will she have to swim to reach the opposite bank at a right angle?

(b) What will her actual speed be?

(a) $\sin \theta = \dfrac{\text{opp}}{\text{hyp}}$

$\sin \theta = \dfrac{2}{2.5}$

$\therefore \theta = 53.1°$ ← Use $\sin^{-1}$ key

Angle required = $90° - 53.1° = 36.9°$

(b) Resultant speed = $\sqrt{2.5^2 - 2^2}$ ← Use Pythagoras' theorem

$= \sqrt{6.25 - 4}$

$= \sqrt{2.25} = 1.5$m/s

PROGRESS CHECK

1. What is the column vector for each of these?

   (a)   **(b)**   **(c)**   **(d)**

2. $\mathbf{e} = \begin{pmatrix} -2 \\ 3 \end{pmatrix}$ $\mathbf{f} = \begin{pmatrix} 4 \\ -1 \end{pmatrix}$ $\mathbf{g} = \begin{pmatrix} 3 \\ 2 \end{pmatrix}$

   Find...

   (a) $\mathbf{e} + \mathbf{f}$ **(b)** $\mathbf{e} - \mathbf{f}$ **(c)** $\mathbf{e} + \mathbf{f} + \mathbf{g}$ **(d)** $\mathbf{g} - \mathbf{e}$.

3. Four points are plotted and joined to form a quadrilateral
   P(4, 4); Q (0, 4); R(-4, -4); S(4, 0)

   (a) What are the column vectors for $\vec{PQ}$, $\vec{QR}$, $\vec{PS}$, $\vec{SR}$?

   (b) What shape is formed?

   (c) What can you say about the sides of PQRS?

   (d) M is the point where the diagonals of PQRS intersect. If $\vec{QR} = \mathbf{c}$ and $\vec{QP} = \mathbf{b}$, write down the two diagonals in terms of **b** and **c**.

4. A boy wants to row his boat to a point directly across a river. The water is flowing at 2.5m/s. If there is no current, he can row the boat at 5.5m/s. What is his resultant speed and the angle, with the river bank, that he needs to row to reach his given point?

Sample GCSE questions

Unit 3

1 This is a plan of a garden. The shading is a path across the garden. The rest of the garden is grass.

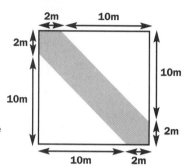

Diagram not drawn to scale

(a) Jacob wants to put fencing down one side of the garden. Find the length of fencing he will need. **(1)**

(b) Calculate the area of the garden. **(1)**

(c) What area of the square is grass? What percentage is this of the total garden? **(2)**

(d) What is the area of the path? What fraction is this of the total garden? **(2)**

(a) Length of fencing = 2 + 10 = 12m

(b) Area = 12 × 12 = 144m^2

(c) Grass area = 10 × 10 = 100m^2

  percentage of the total garden = $\frac{100}{144} \times 100\% = 69.4\%$

(d) Path area = 144 – 100 = 44m^2

  fraction of the total garden = $\frac{44}{144} = \frac{11}{36}$

The grass area is a square of side 10m made up of two identical triangles

Unit 3

2 Factory A and factory B each supply windscreen wiper blades to garages. The graph shows how much each charges for their goods.

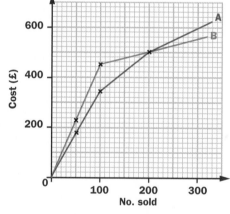

Think about what is happening when the links cross over each other

(a) (i) How much does factory A charge for 50 wiper blades? **(1)**

  (ii) If you need 100 wiper blades, which factory would you go to to get the cheapest blades? **(1)**

(b) Two garages X and Y buy some wiper blades.

  (i) X spends £300 on wiper blades.
  How many could they buy from factory B?
  How many more could they buy from factory A? **(2)**

  (ii) 200 wiper blades cost the same from factory A and factory B.
  Garage Y buys 200 wiper blades.
  They sell them at £3.99 each and want to know when they will cover their original cost. How many wiper blades do they have to sell to do this? **(3)**

Sample GCSE questions

(a) (i) £180

(ii) Factory A because factory A charges £350 whereas factory B charges £450

(b) (i) £300 buys 65 wiper blades from factory B; £300 buys 90 wiper blades from factory A

∴ 25 more could be bought from A than B.

Read this data off the graph

(ii) 200 wiper blades cost £500

500 ÷ 3.99 = 125.31 ≈ 126 wiper blades

126 wiper blades sold at £3.99 will cover the original cost.

Unit 3

3 Nikki is investigating the size of angles.

She draws three angles at a point: one acute angle, one obtuse angle and one reflex angle. This is her drawing:

(a) Measure the acute angle. **(1)**

(b) Measure the obtuse angle. **(1)**

(c) What do you think the reflex angle will be? Give a reason for your answer. **(2)**

(a) Acute angle   = 30°

(b) Obtuse angle = 95°

(c) Reflex angle = 235° (angles at a point add up to 360°)

Unit 3

4 Areas of land can be measured in hectares.

1 hectare (ha) = 100m × 100m or 10 000m^2

(a) This diagram represents an area of 1 hectare. Why? Explain your answer. **(1)**

40m

0.25km

Diagrams not drawn to scale

(b) A farmer's field is shaped like a T and has an area of 1 hectare. Find length 't'. **(3)**

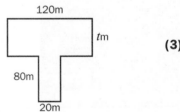

120m

tm

80m

20m

(a) 0.25km = 250m

Area = 250 × 40 = 10 000m^2 = 1 hectare

Divide the area into two rectangles

(b) Area = (80 × 20) + (120 × t) = 10 000m^2

1600 + 120t = 10 000

120t = 10 000 − 1600 = 8400

12t = 840

t = 70m

Sample GCSE questions

Unit 3

You may be asked to leave your answer in terms of π – always read the question carefully

5 A bicycle wheel has a diameter of 75cm. What is its circumference? **(2)**

To find circumference use $C = \pi d$

$C = \pi \times 75$

$\quad = 236$cm to the nearest cm

Unit 3

6 (a) Explain why the exterior angle (e) of a regular octagon is 45° **(1)**

(b) Two congruent regular octagons are joined as shown. Work out the size of angle f. **(2)**

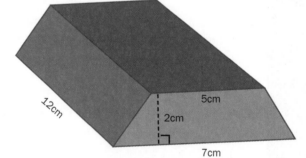

(a) Sum of the eight exterior angles of the octagon = 360°

$\therefore$ exterior angle (e) = $\dfrac{360°}{8}$ = 45°

(b) Angle f = 2 × exterior angle = 2 × 45° = 90°

Unit 3

7 A bar of chocolate is in the shape shown in the diagram. Its cross-section is a trapezium.

Remember this is a prism

Not drawn to scale

12cm

5cm

2cm

7cm

(a) Calculate the area of the cross-section. **(2)**

(b) The mass of the chocolate bar is 230g. Work out the density of the chocolate. Give your answer in g/cm³. **(4)**

To find the density you need to work out the volume first

(a) Area of cross-section = $\dfrac{1}{2}$ (5 + 7) × 2 = 12cm²

(b) Volume of bar = area of cross-section × length

$\quad\quad\quad\quad = 12 \times 12 = 144$cm³

$\quad$ Density = $\dfrac{\text{mass}}{\text{volume}}$

$\quad\quad\quad\quad = \dfrac{230}{144}$

$\quad\quad\quad\quad = 1.6$g/cm³

Exam practice questions

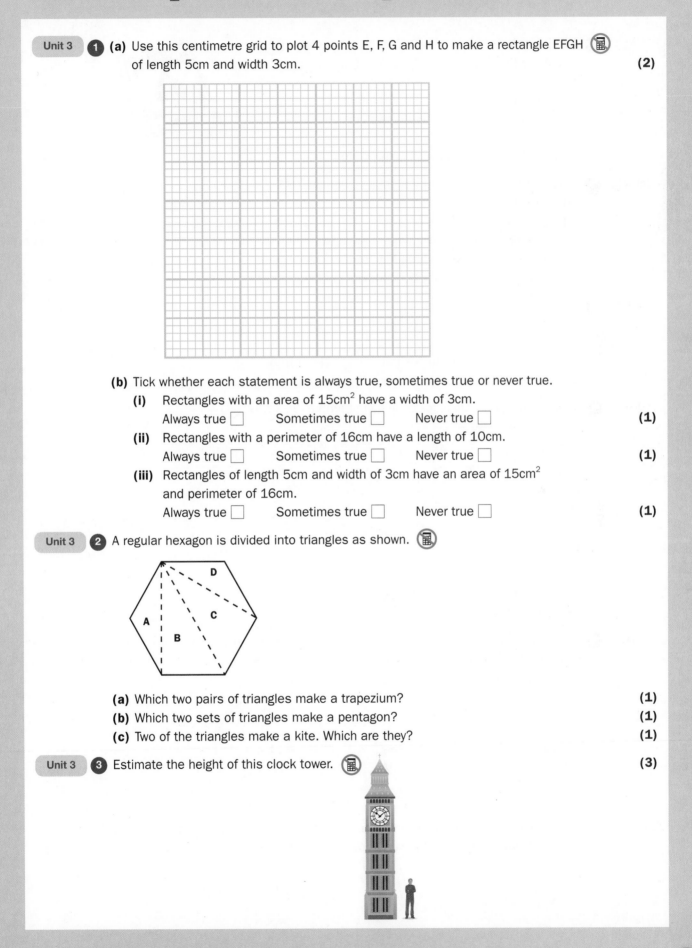

Unit 3 ① **(a)** Use this centimetre grid to plot 4 points E, F, G and H to make a rectangle EFGH of length 5cm and width 3cm. **(2)**

(b) Tick whether each statement is always true, sometimes true or never true.

(i) Rectangles with an area of 15cm^2 have a width of 3cm.

Always true ☐   Sometimes true ☐   Never true ☐ **(1)**

(ii) Rectangles with a perimeter of 16cm have a length of 10cm.

Always true ☐   Sometimes true ☐   Never true ☐ **(1)**

(iii) Rectangles of length 5cm and width of 3cm have an area of 15cm^2 and perimeter of 16cm.

Always true ☐   Sometimes true ☐   Never true ☐ **(1)**

Unit 3 ② A regular hexagon is divided into triangles as shown.

(a) Which two pairs of triangles make a trapezium? **(1)**

(b) Which two sets of triangles make a pentagon? **(1)**

(c) Two of the triangles make a kite. Which are they? **(1)**

Unit 3 ③ Estimate the height of this clock tower. **(3)**

Exam practice questions

Unit 3 **4** A pack of playing cards is in the shape of a cuboid.

length = 8.5cm

width = 5.5cm

height = 1.5cm

The packs fit exactly into a carton with dimensions:

length = 22cm, width = 17cm, height = 12cm

Work out the number of packs in the carton. **(4)**

Unit 3 **5** Suggest units to measure the average speed of:

   (a) a marathon runner **(1)**

   (b) a cat chasing a mouse **(1)**

   (c) an express train travelling from London to Leeds **(1)**

   (d) an aeroplane travelling from New York to Los Angeles **(1)**

   (e) a ship sailing from Hong Kong to New Zealand **(1)**

Unit 3 **6** Tick whether the following statement is always true, sometimes true or never true.

The perimeter of a rectangle of length 8cm is greater than the circumference of a circle, diameter 8cm.

Always true ☐   Sometimes true ☐   Never true ☐ **(2)**

Give an explanation for your answer.

Unit 3 **7** A square paper napkin is folded in half to form a rectangle.

The perimeter of the rectangle = 30cm

What is the area of the square napkin? **(4)**

Unit 3 **8** An Indian restaurant serves poppadoms with its meals. The poppadoms are circular and very thin. There are three sizes of poppadom: 15cm diameter, 20cm diameter and 30cm diameter.

Raj wants a 30cm poppadom, but his friends persuade him to have one each of the 15cm and 20cm, saying he will get more poppadom. Are they correct? Show your working. **(4)**

Exam practice questions

Unit 3 **9** Show that y = 15mm (2)

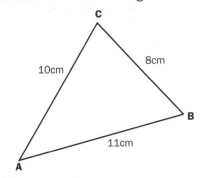

Unit 3 **10** Triangle ABC has AB = 11cm, BC = 8cm, AC = 10cm.
Calculate the smallest angle in the triangle. (3)

Unit 3 **11** A photograph is taken with a digital camera. Its size on the computer screen is 21cm by
15cm. Calculate the scale factor of enlargement if photographs of the following sizes are
required for printing.
 (a) 10.5cm by 7.5cm (1)
 (b) 15.75cm by 11.25cm (1)
 (c) 26.25cm by 18.75cm (1)
 (d) 31.5cm by 22.5cm (1)
 (e) 42cm by 30cm (1)

Unit 3 **12** O is the centre of the circle.
$\angle$ MPR = 126°

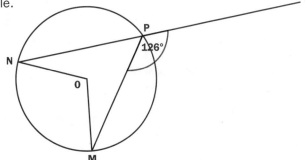

Work out the size of the reflex angle MON.
Show all working. (3)

Unit 3 **13** An aircraft flies from an airport, H, on a bearing of 285° for 300km to airport M.
It then has to fly to airport G, on a bearing of 300°, for 200km.
Use a scale drawing to answer the following:
 (a) What is the total distance flown?
 (b) What is the bearing of H from G? (5)

Exam practice answers

Statistics and probability

1. **(a)** Sales were probably greatest in December because of Christmas.
   (b) Total sales to men = 100 000
   Total sales to women = 102 000
   ∴ No, he is not correct.

2. The range of girls' scores = 40 − 18 = 22
   The mean of girls' scores
   = [(2 × 18) + 22 + (3 × 24) + (2 × 36) + 38 + 40] ÷ 10
   = 280 ÷ 10 = 28
   The range and mean of girls' scores are both similar to those of the boys, although marginally less. There is no real difference, so the hypothesis is not true.

3. **(a)** Mean grade = [(1 × 1) + (2 × 2) + (3 × 10) + (4 × 18) + (5 × 15) + (6 × 4)] ÷ 50
      = 206 ÷ 50 = 4.12
      ∴ mean grade is 4
   (b)(i) Median is 13th value which is in grade 3.
   (ii) Yes. 19 students achieved one of the top three grades at violin. 15 students achieved one of the top three grades at recorder.

4. **(a)** Positive
   (b) Negative
   (c) Positive
   (d) Zero
   (e) Negative
   (f) Positive

5. *(Remember to plot the points at the middle of the class interval. You can draw a histogram first, but it is not necessary unless requested.)*
   (a)
   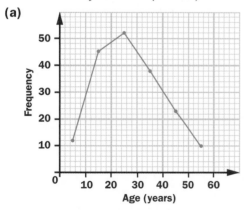
   (b) Modal class = $20 < a \leqslant 30$
   (c) Mean age = 27.5 years
   (d) Median is in class interval $20 < a \leqslant 30$
   (e) The CD appeals most to the 20 to 30 year olds.

6. **(a)** 160
   (b) 16
   (c) 16.7%
   (d) $\frac{54}{360} = \frac{3}{20}$
   (e)(i) P(fizzy drink) = $\frac{120}{360} = \frac{1}{3}$
   (ii) P(milk or a hot drink) = $\frac{60}{360} + \frac{36}{360} = \frac{96}{360} = \frac{4}{15}$

7. **(a)**

Exam marks	Frequency	Cumulative frequency
0–10	0	0
11–20	3	3
21–30	4	7
31–40	20	27
41–50	29	56
51–60	25	81
61–70	16	97
71–80	3	100

   (b)
   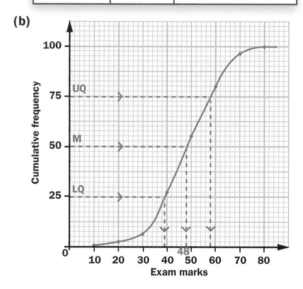
   (c) Pass mark = 60% of 80 = 0.6 × 80 = 48
   Number of students who pass the exam
   = 100 − 50 = 50   (see graph)
   (d) Median mark = 48
   Upper quartile = 58, lower quartile = 39,
   inter-quartile range = 58 − 39 = 19 (see graph)
   (e)
   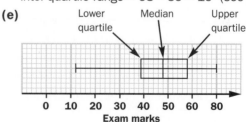
   (f) 50% of marks are between 39 and 58

192

8. (a) Any suitable questions, for example:
   What is your age?
   (give tick boxes for different age groups)
   Do you want a take-away restaurant in this area?
   (give tick boxes for Yes, No, Don't know)
   What opening hours would be suitable for the
   area? (give tick boxes for different time slots)
   (b) Make sure sample is representative of
   different age groups, gender, local districts on
   the estate.

9. (a) (i) 780
   (ii) £191.50
   (b) (i) P(20p coin) $= \frac{140}{780} = \frac{7}{39}$

   (ii) P(£1 coin) $= \frac{54}{780} = \frac{9}{130}$

   (iii) P(1p or a 2p coin) $= \frac{150}{780} + \frac{200}{780} = \frac{350}{780} = \frac{35}{78}$

10. (a) P(W open) = 1 – (0.25 + 0.35 + 0.2) = 0.2
   (b) P(N or S open) = 0.25 + 0.35 = 0.6
   (c) P(W not open) = 1 – 0.2 = 0.8

11. (a)

Outcome

   (b) P(two fiction books)
   = 0.68 × 0.68 = 0.4624 = 0.462 to 3 s.f.
   (c) P(at least one fiction book)
   = (0.68 × 0.68) + (0.68 × 0.32) + (0.32 × 0.68)
   = 0.4624 + 0.2176 + 0.2176
   = 0.8976
   = 0.898 to 3 s.f.

Number

1. (a) Second food processor costs £97.50 + VAT
   = 97.50 × 1.175   *(100% + 17½% = 1.175)*
   = £114.56
   First food processor is the better deal.
   (b) Sale price = £110.95 – £20 = £90.95
   Percentage decrease $= \frac{£20}{£110.95} \times 100\%$
   = 18.03 = 18%

2. Instant saver account = 15 250 × 2 × 0.0325
                              = £991.25
   15 250 + 991.25 = £16 241.25
   2 year account = 15 250(1.0415)^2 = £16 542.01
   2 year account is better for Al as £300.76 more
   interest.

3. (a) (i) 78.41 ÷ 23.79 ≈ 80 ÷ 20 = 4
   (ii) 78.41 ÷ 23.79 = 3.295 922 657 = 3.30
        to 2 d.p.
   (b) (i) 223.8 × 0.0047 ≈ 220 × 0.005 = 1.1
   (ii) 223.8 × 0.0047 = 1.051 86 = 1.05 to 2 d.p.
   (c) (i) $\frac{27.6 \times 30.51}{11.2 \times 2.71} \approx \frac{30 \times 30}{10 \times 3} = 30$

   (ii) $\frac{27.6 \times 30.51}{11.2 \times 2.71} = 27.743 674 22 = 27.74$ to
        2 d.p.
   (d) (i) $\frac{52^2}{9.8^3} \approx \frac{50 \times 50}{10 \times 10 \times 10} = \frac{2500}{1000} = 2.5$

   (ii) $\frac{52^2}{9.8^3} = 2.872 952 596 = 2.87$ to 2 d.p.

4. (a) Ratio of volumes = ratio of radii cubed
        = 1 : 10^3 = 1 : 1000
   (b) Ratio of densities $= \frac{\text{ratio of mass}}{\text{ratio of volume}}$
        $= \frac{\frac{1}{100}}{\frac{1}{1000}} = \frac{1}{0.1} = 1 : 0.1$
   (c) Radius of Earth = 6.378 × 10^{6}m
        Radius of Saturn = 6.0268 × 10^{7}m
   (d) $\frac{\text{Mass of Earth}}{\text{Mass of Saturn}} = \frac{5.97 \times 10^{24}}{5.69 \times 10^{26}}$
        = 1.049 209 139 × 10^{-2}
        = 1.05 x 10^{-2}

5. (a) Belfast was the warmest place.
   (b) (i) London to Glasgow: -7°C   *(Always take
        care when working with negative numbers)*
   (ii) Belfast to Oxford: -5°C
   (iii) Glasgow to Manchester: +6°C
        *(You are asked for the difference so include
        + to show increase)*

6. (a) (i) Multiples of 5: 35, 40, 55, 80
   (ii) Factor of 32: 4
   (iii) Square numbers: 4, 49
   (iv) $\frac{2}{5}$ as a percentage: 40(%)
   (b) 80 ÷ (55 – 4 – 35) × 49 = 80 ÷ 16 × 49 = 245

7. Pears cost 4 × 35p = £1.40
   Oranges cost 3 × 50p = £1.50
   Total spent = £1.40 + £1.50 = £2.90
   Change = £5 – £2.90 = £2.10

8. Fiona's age $= \frac{5}{8} \times 64 = 5 \times 8 = 40$yrs
   Benjamin's age $= \frac{3}{16} \times 64 = 3 \times 4 = 12$yrs
   Fiona's age – Benjamin's age = 40 – 12 = 28yrs

9. **(a)** $\sqrt{36} \times \sqrt[3]{27} = 6 \times 3 = 18$

   (b) $7^2 = 49$

   (c) First statement is true: $3^2 = 9$, $11^2 = 121$, etc.

10. **(a)** $\frac{1}{3} + \frac{3}{5} = \frac{5}{15} + \frac{9}{15} = \frac{14}{15}$

    (b) $\frac{\sqrt{101}}{21} \approx \frac{\sqrt{100}}{20} = \frac{10}{20} = \frac{1}{2}$ or 0.5

11. Each row, column and diagonal = $10 + 3 + 14 = 27$

    $a = 27 - (10 + 13) = 4$

    $b = 27 - (14 + 5) = 8$

    $c = 27 - (a + b) = 27 - (4 + 8) = 15$

    $d = 27 - (13 + 5) = 9$

12. 5 parts of the ratio = £3200

    1 part of the ratio = £3200 ÷ 5 = £640

    Total number of parts = 8 parts; 8 × £640 = £5120

13. **(a)** Articles are $1 - (\frac{1}{5} + \frac{1}{3}) = 1 - \frac{8}{15} = \frac{7}{15}$

    (b) Number of graphs = $\frac{5}{9} \times 36 = 20$

14. **(a)** $(3 + \sqrt{5})(3 + \sqrt{5}) = 9 + 6\sqrt{5} + 5 = 14 + 6\sqrt{5}$

    (b) $\frac{\sqrt{48} + 24}{\sqrt{12}} = \frac{\sqrt{48}}{\sqrt{12}} + \frac{24}{\sqrt{12}}$

    $= \sqrt{4} + \frac{2 \times 12}{\sqrt{(4 \times 3)}} = 2 + \frac{12}{\sqrt{3}}$

    (Multiply top and bottom of $\frac{12}{\sqrt{3}}$ by $\sqrt{3}$ to get $\frac{12\sqrt{3}}{3}$
    $= 4\sqrt{3}$)

    $= 2 + 4\sqrt{3} = 2(1 + 2\sqrt{3})$

15. **(a)** 3.04, 3.14, 3.41, 3.411

    (b) -7, -3, 1, 3, 5

    (c) $\frac{1}{4}, \frac{1}{3}, \frac{3}{8}, \frac{1}{2}$

    (d) 0.24, 0.3, $\frac{2}{5}, \frac{5}{8}$

16. **(a)** $2\frac{5}{8} > 2.525$

    (b) -0.78 < -0.65

    (c) $\frac{22}{7} = 3.14$ (to 2 d.p.)

    (d) 0.001 963 > 0.0016

17. **(a)** £10 buys $16 so £50 buys $(5 × 16) = $80

    (You can work out the rate for £1 instead)

    (b) $30 buys £18 so $5 buys £(18 ÷ 6) = £3

    $80 buys £(3 × 16) = £48

    (c) Iqra lost £2 by having to exchange back from dollars to pounds.

    (d) Percentage loss = $\frac{2}{50} \times 100 = 4\%$

Algebra

1. **(a)** $9c + 4d + de$

   (b) $5m + n + mn$

   (c) $7xy$

   (d) $-18p^3q^2$

   (e) $-12a - 9b$

2. **(a)** 9

   (b) 17

   (c) -1

   (d) 12

   (e) 0

3. **(a)** True

   (b) False, $p - q$

   (c) False, cde

   (d) True

   (e) True

4. **(a)** $p = 0 + 3$, $p = 3$

   (b) $q = 4 \times 2$, $q = 8$

   (c) $3r - 2 = 13$

   $3r = 13 + 2 = 15$

   $r = 5$

5. **(a)** $7 \times 2 = 14$, $14 + 3 = 17$

   $17 \times 2 = 34$, $34 + 3 = 37$

   next two terms are 17, 37

   (b) The next three terms are 6, 9, 12

   (c) Constant difference of sequence terms = 3

   term 1 = $2 + (0 \times 3)$

   term 2 = $2 + (1 \times 3)$

   term 3 = $2 + (2 \times 3)$

   term n = $2 + (n - 1) \times 3 = 2 + 3n - 3$

   nth term = $3n - 1$

6. **(a)** $3a - a^2 = a(3 - a)$

   (b) $49 - b^2 = (7 + b)(7 - b)$ *(difference of two squares)*

   (c) $5 + 3c = 6 - c$

   $c + 3c = 6 - 5$

   $4c = 1$

   $c = \frac{1}{4}$

   (d) $\frac{x + 3}{3} - \frac{x - 2}{4} = \frac{7}{4}$

   $4(x + 3) - 3(x - 2) = 7 \times 3$

   (look for a denominator common to all three fractions)

   $4x + 12 - 3x + 6 = 21$

   $x = 21 - 18 = 3$

7. (a) $x < 4$

(b) $x \geq -3$

(c) $-2 \leq x < 1$

(d) $2x - 1 > 5$

(e) $4 \geq y - 1 > 1$

8. (a) $2y = -5x$ *(compare with $y = mx + c$)*

$y = \frac{-5}{2}x$ *(divide both sides by 2)*

The coefficient of $x = \frac{-5}{2}$

gradient $= \frac{-5}{2}$ or -2.5

y-intercept $= 0$

(This line passes through the origin as $c = 0$)

(b) $2y = 4x + 1$ $y = \frac{6x + 4}{3}$ $y = x - 2$

Rearrange all equations to general equation

$y = mx + c$

$y = 2x + \frac{1}{2}$ $y = 2x + \frac{4}{3}$ $y = x - 2$

No, the first two equations are parallel as their gradients (m) are equal.

9. (a) $2x + 9$ *(treat these the same as ordinary fractions)*

(b) $31a + 7$

(c) $9b + 4$

10. (a) Number of runs $= 6a + 4b + c$

(b) $T = (P - Q)p$ pence or $T = £\frac{(P - Q)p}{100}$

(c) $a + (a + 1) + (a + 2) = 48$ or $3a + 3 = 48$

11. (a) Let the two numbers be a and b

$a + b = 27$ ①

$a - b = 3$ ②

① + ②   *(eliminate b)*

$2a = 30$

$a = 15$

substitute in ①

$15 + b = 27$

$b = 27 - 15 = 12$

(b) Let the number of expensive seats be e

Let the number of cheaper seats be c

$e + c = 500$ ①

$8e - 5c = 100$ ②

$5e + 5c = 2500$ ③   (① × 5 giving ③)

② + ③   *(eliminate c)*

$13e = 2600$

$e = 200$

substitute in ①

$200 + c = 500$

$c = 500 - 200$

$c = 300$

There are 200 seats at £8 and 300 seats at £5.

(always give the answer in context)

12. (a) $3(x - 1) + (x + 2) = 2(x + 2)(x - 1)$

$3x - 3 + x + 2 = 2x^2 + 2x - 4$

$4x - 1 = 2x^2 + 2x - 4$

giving $2x^2 - 2x - 3 = 0$

use the quadratic formula $x = \frac{-b \pm \sqrt{b^2 - 4ac}}{2a}$

$x = \frac{-(-2) \pm \sqrt{(-2)^2 - (4 \times 2 \times -3)}}{2 \times 2}$

$x = \frac{2 \pm \sqrt{4 + 24}}{4}$

$x = \frac{2 \pm \sqrt{28}}{4}$

solutions: either $x = \frac{2 + \sqrt{28}}{4}$ or $x = \frac{2 - \sqrt{28}}{4}$

either $x = 1.82$ or $= -0.82$ (to 2 d.p.)

(b) $5x + y = 14$ ①

$2x - y = 7$ ②

① + ②   *(eliminate y)*

giving $7x = 21$

$x = 3$

substitute in ①

giving $15 + y = 14$

$y = 14 - 15 = -1$

(c) $2x^2 - 5x - 12 = 0$

$(2x + 3)(x - 4) = 0$ *(try factors of 12 and remember to watch the signs)*

$x = \frac{-3}{2} = -1\frac{1}{2}$

or $x = 4$

Exam practice answers

13.

x	-2	-1	0	1	2
y	-12	-5	-4	-3	4

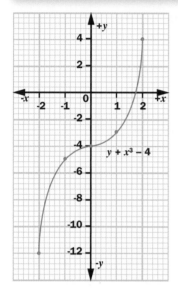

14. $3x + 2y = 7$ $x + y = 3$

x	-1	0	1
y	5	3.5	2

x	-1	0	1
y	4	3	2

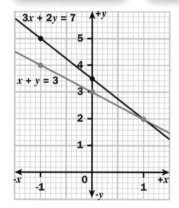

$x = 1, y = 2$

15. (a) (0, 3)

(b) (0, -1)

(c) (-2, 1)

(d) (2, 1)

Geometry and measures

1. (a) Any rectangle with length 5cm and width 3cm

(b)(i) Sometimes true

(ii) Never true

(iii) Always true

2. (a) A and B or C and D

(b) A, B and C or B, C and D

(c) B and C

3. Height of the man ≈ 2 metres

∴ height of clock tower ≈ 4 x 2 = 8 metres

4. Length of carton = 4 × width of pack

Width of carton = 2 × length of pack

Height of carton = 8 × height of pack

Number of packs = 4 × 2 × 8 = 64

5. (a) km/h

(b) m/s

(c) mph or km/h

(d) mph or km/h

(e) km/h (or knots)

6. Statement is sometimes true. It depends on the width of the rectangle. If the width is greater than 4.5 the perimeter is greater than the circumference. If the width is less than 4.5 the perimeter is smaller than the circumference.

7. Let side of square = s cm

perimeter of rectangle = $2(s + \frac{s}{2})$

$$= 2 \times \frac{3s}{2}$$
$$= 3s = 30\text{cm}$$
$$\therefore s = \frac{30}{3} = 10\text{cm}$$

area of napkin = $s \times s = 10 \times 10 = 100\text{cm}^2$

8. Area of 15cm poppadom = $\pi \times 7.5^2 = 56.25\pi$

Area of 20cm poppadom = $\pi \times 10^2 = 100\pi$

Area of 30cm poppadom = $\pi \times 15^2 = 225\pi$

No, they are not correct as $100\pi + 56.25\pi < 225\pi$

9. Using Pythagoras' theorem:

$y^2 = 39^2 - 36^2$

$= 1521 - 1296 = 225$

$y = \sqrt{225}$

$= 15\text{mm}$

10. Smallest angle is opposite shortest side.

Using cosine rule: $a^2 = b^2 + c^2 - 2bc \cos A$

$\cos A = \frac{10^2 + 11^2 - 8^2}{2(10 \times 11)}$

$= \frac{100 + 121 - 64}{220}$

$= \frac{157}{220} = 0.7136$

$\angle A = \cos^{-1} 0.7136 = 44.5°$ *(use shift cos for cos^{-1})*

11. (a) $\frac{1}{2}$ or 0.5

(b) $\frac{3}{4}$ or 0.75

(c) $1\frac{1}{4}$ or $\frac{5}{4}$ or 1.25

(d) $1\frac{1}{2}$ or $\frac{3}{2}$ or 1.5

(e) 2

12. ∠ NPM = 180° − 126° = 54°

(angles on a straight line add up to 180°)

obtuse ∠ MON = 2 × 54° = 108°

(angle at the centre of circle is twice that at circumference)

reflex ∠ MON = 360° − 108° = 252°

(angles at a point add up to 360°)

13. (a) Total distance = 500km

(b) 110°

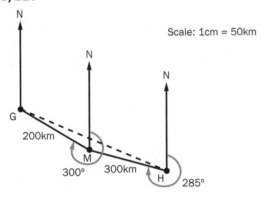

Scale: 1cm = 50km

Notes

Index

Index